In Christ
All Things Hold Together

The Intersection of Science & Christian Theology

A REPORT OF THE COMMISSION ON THEOLOGY AND CHURCH RELATIONS

THE LUTHERAN CHURCH—MISSOURI SYNOD   FEBRUARY 2015

The Intersection of Science and Christian Theology: Abbreviations

AC *Augsburg Confession*
AE *Luther's Works*. American ed. 55 vols. St. Louis: Concordia and Philadelphia: Fortress, 1955–1986.
Ap Apology of the Augsburg Confession
FC ep Formula of Concord, Epitome
FC SD Formula of Concord, Solid Declaration
LC The Large Catechism

In Christ All Things Hold Together

The Intersection of Science and Christian Theology

In Christ All Things Hold Together

The Intersection of Science and Christian Theology

* * * * * *

Introduction: The Challenge of Scientism

Contemporary Western culture is increasingly influenced by the doctrine of *scientism*. Scientism does not merely assert that empirical science is *a* generally reliable source of information about the natural world, a claim that is uncontroversial. Rather, scientism claims that a particular approach to science—the materialistic science which has become dominant since the Enlightenment—is the *only* way to gain knowledge.[1] While a modest empirical approach sees science as a useful, but limited instrument to be complemented by the findings of other disciplines (such as literature, philosophy and theology), scientism claims that a materialistic paradigm of investigation has a monopoly on human knowledge. The consequence is that metaphysics, religion, and even traditional ethics lose their cognitive status and appear vulnerable to replacement by more enlightened thinking.

At an institutional level, we see this in the radical disconnect between the sciences and the humanities noted by C. P. Snow in his classic work, *The Two Cultures*.[2] Scientists and non-scientists receive very different educations, with very little by way of overlap that would facilitate dialogue between the sciences and other disciplines. Increasingly, scientists are given a highly specialized, technical training, and have little time to ponder the broader questions of human nature and the human condition. At the same time, many students in the humanities are scientifically illiterate and easily confuse ideological claims made on behalf of science with what the science itself is saying. As a result, cultural conversations about the value and purpose of science are often unproductive, as neither sort of education produces individuals who have a good understanding of both the science and the broader moral, legal, and theological considerations necessary to guide its best use.

---

[1] The second definition of scientism in the current Random House Dictionary emphasizes this claim: "the belief that the assumptions, methods of research, etc. of the physical and biological sciences are equally appropriate and essential to all other disciplines, including the humanities and social sciences." scientism. Dictionary.com. *Dictionary.com Unabridged*. Random House, Inc. *http://dictionary.reference.com/browse/scientism* (accessed: January 29, 2015).

[2] C. P. Snow, *The Two Cultures* (Cambridge: Cambridge University Press, 2012). This book was developed in two parts, written in 1959 (the Rede Lectures) and 1964 ("The Two Cultures: A Second Look."). While Snow's work on the "disconnect" noted here has typically framed this discussion, his views on the intersection of science and non-science have not gone unchallenged. The arguments in this document are not contingent on his framework.

Scientism exacerbates this problem as it leads people to regard literature, philosophy and religion as unverifiable relics of our pre-scientific past, sources which can no longer contribute to a serious conversation about what is really true. At a personal level, scientism is one of many factors that explain the radical privatization of faith observed by so many of the most astute Christian cultural critics.[3] For Harry Blamires, the problem is that Christians have acquiesced to a one-sided treaty with secularism, according to which religious believers can retain the therapeutic benefits of belief in the supernatural within the privacy of their own minds, provided secular ideologies define public fact.

> Modern secular thought ignores the reality beyond this world ... Secularism is, by its very nature, rooted in this world, accounting it the only sure basis of knowledge, the only reliable source of meaning and value... Hence the collision between the Christian faith and contemporary secular culture. For all teaching of Christian revelation deals with the breaking-in of the greater supernatural order upon our more limited finite world... Secularism is so rooted in this world that it does not allow for the existence of any other. Therefore whenever secularism encounters the Christian mind, either the Christian mind will momentarily shake that rootedness, or secularism will seduce the Christian mind to a temporary mode of converse which overlooks the supernatural.[4]

Blamires's point is that even Christians may start to think that the supernatural is irrelevant to their daily life, so that they no longer see God's providential hand in nature or in their work as a sacred calling to serve others made in the image of God. In this way, complains Blamires, "the Christian mind has allowed itself to be subtly secularized by giving a purely chronological status to the eternal. That is to say, the Christian has relegated the significance of the eternal to the life that succeeds this one."[5] Thus God is no longer seen at work in ordinary events and in each person's vocation.

Similarly, Francis Schaeffer[6] and Nancy Pearcey[7] describe the splitting of the Christian mind into a structure of two levels or stories. The lower story of objective fact is controlled by materialistic science. Since religion and

---

[3] Stephen L. Carter also points to the way the law and our political dialogue has contributed to the privatization of faith in his *The Culture of Disbelief: How American Law and Politics Trivialize Religious Devotion* (New York: Basic Books, 1993).

[4] Harry Blamires, *The Christian Mind: How Should a Christian Think?* (Ann Arbor: Servant Publications, 1978), 67–68.

[5] Ibid., 69.

[6] Francis Schaeffer, *The God Who Is There* (Downers Grove, IL: Intervarsity Press, 1968).

[7] Nancy Pearcey, *Total Truth: Liberating Christianity from Its Cultural Captivity* (Wheaton, IL: Crossway Books, 2004).

transcendent moral claims cannot be investigated in this fashion, they are relegated to the upper story of private values. This upper story can only be accessed by faith, and its contents are regarded as subjective and not the sort of thing which can be known as fact. As Schaeffer said, the assumption of many in our time is that "Rationality and Faith are totally out of contact with each other."[8]

The sad consequence for Christians in the sciences (including students, teachers and workers in the public and private sectors) is that they lose the ability to connect their faith with their work at the *cognitive* level—at the level of how they think—so that they can reasonably claim to know that the world really is as they believe it in faith to be. Thus, while they may continue to see themselves as motivated by a desire to serve their neighbor in God-pleasing ways, it is inconceivable that a biblical worldview could contribute to the framework of assumptions on which scientific *knowledge* is built. Even Christians who are not scientists are greatly affected. The contemporary, pluralized, post-Christian societies typical in the West have no clear center of cultural authority, but amid the babel of voices competing for dominance, scientism has become stronger. A proper respect for scientific rigor may be supplanted by an uncritical acceptance of claims made on behalf of science by secularists in the media and by popular science writers and philosophers with non-Christian agendas (including atheism and a more "inclusive" spirituality). For example, it is increasingly claimed that science has discovered a genetic or neurological "explanation" for religious and moral beliefs.[9] This corrosive environment also tends to push faith inside, making it seem irrational, irrelevant to objective reality and unfit to enter public life, from which government may be only too happy to expunge its influence.

Some Christians do not have a problem with this state of affairs, as they accept the proposal of Stephen Jay Gould, according to which science and religion define non-overlapping magisteria (NOMA).[10] On this view, religion concerns issues of ultimate value (telling us how to go to heaven), while science tells us how the temporal world operates (how the heavens go). However, this apparently neat division of labor denies that either natural or revealed theology tells us anything factual about the origin of the world, the nature of human beings, or the actions of God in history to save mankind. NOMA is incompatible with a comprehensive biblical worldview, according to which Christianity is a framework of "total truth" about reality. Moreover,

<hr>

[8] Schaeffer, *The God Who Is There*, 61.

[9] For a survey of many such views, and a thoughtful scientifically informed Christian response, see Mario Beauregard and Denyse O'Leary, *The Spiritual Brain* (New York: HarperOne, 2007).

[10] See Stephen Jay Gould, *Rock of Ages: Science and Religion and the Fullness of Life* (New York: Ballantine, 1999), and his "Nonoverlapping Magisteria," *Natural History* 106 (March 1997), 16–22, 60–62. For further discussion of NOMA and other models of relating science and religion, see chapter 3 of this report.

NOMA betrays those Christians in the sciences who are strongly motivated to integrate the content of their Christian faith with their work as scientists. They are not content to live their lives in two tracks—a faith track of devotion and worship, and a work track in which they look at science in exactly the same way as an atheist. To be sure, the basic procedures and standards of competence in science are generally derived from reason, observation, and trial and error, not from Scripture. And there is nothing to be gained by decorating incompetent science with pious platitudes. But sincere Christian scientists[11] do need a way of understanding their work as an authentic calling to understand God's world. This holistic vision of science, in which Christian scientists seek to discover what God has done in the world—in order to glorify Him and use that knowledge to serve others— reconnects the realms of fact and value, of knowledge and meaning, and helps to heal what Martin Marty has called the "modern schism"[12] in the Christian mind.

The hope that such holism can be recovered should not be dismissed as unachievable. Today, national science organizations exert a powerful influence in favor of secularist conformity. However, the history of science provides numerous examples of great scientists who integrated their Christian faith with their scientific work in profoundly illuminating ways. As Alfred North Whitehead argued in *Science and the Modern World*, it was the habitual thought forms of Christendom that made the very idea of modern science appear feasible and worthwhile.

> [T]he greatest contribution of medievalism to the formation of the scientific movement [is] the inexpugnable belief that every detailed occurrence can be correlated with its antecedents in a perfectly definite manner, exemplifying general principles. Without this belief the incredible labours of scientists would be without hope. It is this instinctive conviction, vividly poised before the imagination, which is the motive power of research:—that there is a secret, a secret which can be unveiled. How has this conviction been so vividly implanted on the European mind?

> When we compare this tone of thought in Europe with the attitude of other civilisations when left to themselves, there seems but one source for its origin. It must come from the medieval insistence on the rationality of God, conceived as with the personal energy of Jehovah and with the rationality of a Greek philosopher. Every detail was supervised and ordered: the

---

[11] The term "Christian scientist" refers herein to a scientist who is a Christian, not to a member of the Christian Science religious group.

[12] Martin E. Marty, *The Modern Schism: Three Paths to the Secular* (Eugene, OR: Wipf and Stock, 2012).

search into nature could only result in the vindication of the faith in rationality. [13]

The whole idea that the cosmos is governed by universal rational laws derived from the Christian conviction that all of reality is governed by the will of a single, personal, rational creator who provides for His people, a will which cannot be anticipated by our finite, fallen reason, but must be patiently investigated by empirical means. Early modern scientists saw nature as God's other book. Galileo wrote that the book of nature "was written in the language of mathematics"[14] and that "whatever we read in that book is the creation of the omnipotent Craftsman."[15] Johannes Kepler concurred, going so far as to say that astronomers could learn something of God's providential plan for the world.[16] Appealing to the reformers' emphasis on the priesthood of all believers (1 Pet. 2:9), Kepler saw his scientific work as having devotional value, maintaining that the world was God's temple and that the scientific contemplation of nature was a form of worship.[17]

The contrast between the theologically motivated, faith-inspired scientific vocation of the early modern scientists and the highly specialized, secularized professionalism typical today is a sharp one. The scientism, compartmentalization, cognitive dissonance, disorientation and vocational *angst* found in many contemporary attitudes to science have deep historical roots and require a close analysis of currents in philosophy and theology. The problem of how Christian theology should best engage science is multi-dimensional, requiring close attention to a number of historical and contemporary issues.

From the perspective of the church, perhaps the most troubling feature of scientism is the way it undermines the authority of revelation. The early modern scientists did not see their reason as an autonomous source of secular knowledge about the world, but as a "natural light," a God-given minister to their faith which they employed to the glory of God and for the service of neighbor. However, during the later Enlightenment, religious claims were increasingly dismissed as "superstition." The withering attacks of David Hume, the French Encyclopedists and Higher Criticism assumed that autonomous reason was in a position to judge faith and decide which parts (if any)

---

[13] Alfred North Whitehead, *Science and the Modern World* (New York: New York Free Press, 1997, first published 1925), 13.

[14] Galileo Galilei, *Discoveries and Opinions of Galileo*, trans. Stillman Drake (New York: Doubleday, 1957), 237 f.

[15] Galileo Galilei, *Dialogue Concerning the Two Chief World Systems—Ptolemaic and Copernican*, trans. Stillman Drake (Berkeley: University of California Press, 1962), 3.

[16] Peter Barker, "Astronomy, Providence, and the Lutheran Contribution to Science," in ed. Angus Menuge, *Reading God's World: The Scientific Vocation* (St. Louis: Concordia Publishing House, 2004), 175.

[17] Peter Harrison, "'Priests of the Most High God, with Respect to the Book of Nature': The Vocational Identity of the Early Modern Naturalist," in ed. Angus Menuge, *Reading God's World*, 70.

of it could remain.[18] This approach is manifest today in the tendency of many books on the "problem" of science and religion to assume that the "solution" is to see how religion can be reinterpreted or revised to accommodate the latest scientific findings. The early modern scientists would have found it odd that God's book of nature—as interpreted by finite, fallen reason—would be taken to be authoritative over the inspired, inerrant book of God's Word.

To be sure, the fact that Scripture is supreme in its authority, and the only source and norm for orthodox Christian doctrine, does not mean we are always correct in interpreting Scripture. So it can seem (and may sometimes be) reasonable to consider whether some alternative ways of reading Scripture might make it easier to accept some apparently well-confirmed claim of science. Yet there are dangers here all the same. One of these is the unstated assumption that the best science is on the same level as the Word of God. The problem is that God's Word has an eternal and ultimate validity, while even the best scientific theories are the products of finite, fallen minds and have at most a temporal and penultimate status. A marriage between the eternal Word of God and temporal science is apt to produce a widow as the science changes. And it may also create the false impressions that the Word of God changes with the times, or that science is the arbiter of ultimate truth. In this way, science may supplant Scripture as the source and norm for Christian doctrine and life. When this happens, the church must stand on the Word of God, whatever reaction this may provoke.[19]

The church cannot simply baptize the latest findings of science "Christian," accommodating its teaching to the times. Yet neither does it need to adopt a separatist posture that discourages young people from entering science and which has the unappealing appearance of censoring sources of secular information. A lasting synthesis of penultimate science and ultimate truth cannot be had, because the things of this world are passing away, but only God remains eternally the same. Nor is it wise to follow the Reformed approach of "transforming," "redeeming," or "Christianizing" science, as if we can convert the penultimate into the ultimate. A better approach, and one more consonant with Lutheran theology, is to encourage an ongoing dialogue between Scripture and scientific theories that critically evaluates the strengths and weaknesses of the latter, avoiding both uncritical embrace and uncritical dismissal.[20] It is because we have one foot in eternity that we are free to dialog with any of the world's scientific ideas, appreciating their value in serving our

---

[18] See chapter 2 of this report for a more in-depth account of these secularizing influences.

[19] See chapter 4 of this report for more on the best approach to interpreting scriptural passages with apparent scientific import.

[20] See the discussion of Christ and culture using H. Richard Niebuhr's typologies in chapter 1, pages 28 ff.

neighbor while critiquing any ideologies smuggled along with them.[21] We can see manmade theories as, at best, penultimate shadows and anticipations of the eternal and necessary Word of God, and at worst, as idolatrous traps which provide comfort to those who wish to live as if there is no God. We do not seek a final answer in science, or anywhere else in the space of human ideology. Yet we do maintain that it is in Christ that all things, including the world and the scientist, hold together (Col. 1:17).

The supreme authority of Scripture matters, not merely for its own sake, but also because it is where God's action to save mankind—the Gospel— is disclosed. A second danger of the assumption that Scripture should simply be re-interpreted in light of modern science is that, in some cases, it may (perhaps indirectly and inadvertently) undermine the Gospel. Of grave concern here are well-meaning attempts to harmonize the early chapters of Genesis with some version of evolutionary theory. It is not merely that these efforts seem to make incorrect claims about the Genesis text itself. They also appear to undermine later Pauline explanations of how sin and death entered the world, and how, therefore, humans were rescued from their predicament by the work of Christ.[22] It seems that the magisterial use of reason combined with an impatient desire to solve apparent conflicts between science and religion by developing a "patch" for Genesis may subvert the Christological core of the Scripture—the hermeneutical equivalent of killing the patient by suppressing a troubling symptom.

It is not only in the right-hand kingdom, but also in the kingdom of the left[23] that the implications of scientism are felt. For example, materialistic science rejects the Christian claims that human beings are specially made in the image of God, and specially redeemed by the saving acts of the God-man, Jesus Christ. Consistent with his Darwinian materialism, Peter Singer declares that it is "speciesism" (analogous to racism or sexism) to suppose that there is anything of unique value about human beings.[24] Singer wrote in 1979 that "Human babies are not born self-aware, or capable of grasping that they exist over time. They are not persons," and concluded that "the life of a newborn is of less value than the life of a pig, a dog, or a chimpanzee."[25]

---

[21] An excellent exposition of this approach is Gene Edward Veith, *Loving God With All Your Mind: Thinking as a Christian in the Postmodern World* (Wheaton, IL: Crossway Books, 2003).

[22] On this topic, see the penetrating critique of the theological implications of theistic evolution in Norman C. Nevin, ed., *Should Christians Embrace Evolution? Biblical and Scientific Responses* (Phillipsburg, NJ: P&R Publishing, 2011).

[23] In simplest terms, the "right-hand kingdom" refers to the realm of the church (God's kingdom of grace), where God works through His means of grace (Word and Sacraments) to create and sustain faith in Christ, while the "left-hand kingdom" refers to the realm of secular government and society (God's kingdom of power), where God works to provide and promote order through earthly rulers, structures, means, and institutions.

[24] Peter Singer, *Animal Liberation* (New York: Ecco Books, 2002; first published 1975).

[25] Peter Singer, *Practical Ethics* (Cambridge: Cambridge University Press, 1979), 122–23.

Once human value is grounded in natural capacities (whether physical, psychological or sociological), it is clear that some humans will be more valuable than others, and some humans may be disposed of to maximize the welfare of those that remain. The result of this line of thought is that the idea of universal, inalienable rights for all humans can no longer be sustained.[26] The weak, the vulnerable and the despised may lose their protection. In the face of this threat, the church must confidently proclaim, teach and defend the scriptural basis for human dignity and worth. It must speak up for those who cannot speak for themselves (Prov. 31:8). The church will be greatly assisted in this effort by the support of articulate pro-life scientists, whose authority the culture recognizes.

There is something of a renaissance of apologetics both inside and outside The Lutheran Church—Missouri Synod (LCMS), and this is a great opportunity to forge alliances between theologians, scientists, philosophers, and professional apologists in our church for the sake of defending the faith. While the Word of God has its own authority independent of reason, scientific apologetics can play an important role in creating the intellectual and cultural space that allows the Gospel a fair hearing. To be sure, reason cannot produce faith. But it can clear away misconceptions and refute erroneous worldviews that lead people to reject the Christian claim out of hand. Christian scientists and philosophers can help here by marshaling evidence that this is a created world and that human beings are a special part of it. This task has become more important because of the rise of the New Atheism, which seeks to use materialistic science to discredit revealed religion.

This report will provide guidance and encouragement to a number of constituencies who seek to combat scientism and recover the sense of science as a vocation which glorifies God and provides beneficial services to the neighbor. These constituencies include:

(1) Students, teachers and investigators in the sciences;

(2) Pastors and other church workers who minister to those involved in the sciences in regular congregations and in campus ministry;

(3) Administrators and teachers at Christian high schools and universities who would like input to help them think through the hard task of integrating the Christian faith with science education;

(4) Non-scientific Christian laity whose faith is being attacked as an unscientific relic of the past.

This last group is by no means the least significant, as the authority of science is being used as a cultural weapon and non-scientists are often ill-equipped to defend themselves. As C. S. Lewis wrote in his famous essay, "On

---

[26] For discussion, see Angus J. L. Menuge, "Why Human Rights Cannot Be Naturalized" in *Legitimizing Human Rights: Secular and Religious Perspectives*, ed. Angus J. L. Menuge (Farnham, UK: Ashgate, 2013).

Learning in War-Time," Christian intellectuals have a special responsibility here:

> To be ignorant and simple now—not to be able to meet the enemies on their own ground—would be to throw down our weapons, and to betray our uneducated brethren who have, under God, no defense but us against the intellectual attacks of the heathen.[27]

So the goal of this report is to encourage more informed discussion and dialogue between all parties, those with a science background and those without it, so that the Church is better equipped both to respond to challenges and to encourage more young Christians to pursue scientific vocations.

An overview of the report

This report aims to serve as a constructive resource for thoughtful Christian reflection on the complex questions arising from the intersection of science, faith and Christian theology. Each of its five chapters provides conceptual tools and examples that should aid Christians in forming a faithful response to these questions and, it is hoped, will encourage more young people to pursue scientific careers in full knowledge of the nature and significance of the scientific vocation.

The opening chapter seeks to lay out the rich theological resources for understanding the nature and purpose of science. Since science is a preeminent application of human reason, and faithful Christian scientists are also called to reverence God's Word, the chapter begins with a discussion of the authority of Scripture and the proper role of reason. The argument is made that in science and elsewhere, reason should serve as a servant of Christian faith, rather than as a judge of it. The chapter moves to a consideration of how God's two books—the book of Scripture and the book of nature—relate to one another. How do we give both books their due, while recognizing the supreme authority of Scripture? Next, we explore the implications of the doctrines of vocation and of the two kingdoms for science. This leads naturally into a discussion of the strengths and weaknesses of various models for Christian engagement with culture, and their implications for the work of a scientist. The advantages of a "dialog" model over conflicting alternatives are presented. Then we consider what it means to look at nature in a Christocentric way, and reflect on the implications of image of God theology and other elements of Christian anthropology for the scientific task. The chapter concludes by considering the many theological assumptions that encouraged and guided the rise of modern science.

---

[27] C. S. Lewis, "Learning in War-Time," in *The Weight of Glory and Other Addresses* (New York: Macmillan, 1965), 27–28.

Chapter 1 shows such a close and positive connection between Christian theology and good science that it is important to explain why that connection is not widely appreciated today. So chapter 2 focuses on the historical factors leading to the contemporary perception that faith and theology have nothing to do with scientific practice. That sad story begins with the attack on final causes (purpose, design) in nature and the related decline of natural theology. While natural theology may sometimes have gone too far by reading design into nature that was not there, modern science has largely rejected design as a valid scientific category, which prevents the scientist from ever inferring that we inhabit a created world. This transition was encouraged by the rise of two main ideas: the idea of autonomous reason (reason that no longer was seen as a servant of the faith), and the idea of nature as an autonomous machine, running on by itself, with no need for God. In this intellectual atmosphere, many thinkers moved from orthodox Christianity to deism and even naturalism, the atheistic view that nature alone exists. Soon it seemed to many that materialistic science alone provided reliable knowledge, while theology, philosophy and ethics were all treated with suspicion. Side by side with these ideological changes, science changed as a social institution. While science had been understood as a vocation of reading the book of nature, it was reconceived as a modern profession with a methodology that excluded God's work from a scientific understanding of nature. The fallout of these momentous changes is seen in the unbiblical view of reality prevalent among many young American Christians, the so-called "moralistic therapeutic deism"[28] which keeps God distant from the natural world and our lives, undermining the idea that science is a vocation.

Chapter 2 is a sobering portrayal of how different our intellectual world today is from the era and thought-world of the scientific revolution, in which faithful Christian scientists self-consciously applied theology to their work and found God present everywhere in the world. Chapter 3 provides a constructive response to the philosophical assumptions of our contemporary perspective. It explains the philosophical basis of scientism and how its arguments may be refuted. More positively, several reasons are given for thinking that Christianity provides a superior foundation for science than naturalism: Christian teaching explains why science is feasible, gives scientists the right balance of confidence and humility, restores a sense of meaning in scientific work, explains the reliability of the human mind that is presupposed by science, and provides a strong moral motivation for going into science.

A more difficult and specialized question is how Christians should read specific portions of Scripture with apparent scientific import. This is the topic of chapter 4, which sets out several Lutheran principles of interpretation and

---

[28] Christian Smith and Melinda Denton, *Soul Searching: The Religious and Spiritual Lives of American Teenagers* (New York: Oxford University Press, 2005).

applies them to a number of examples. In the process, advice is given on how to find the right balance between respect for God's Word and humility in the sometimes difficult task of rightly interpreting it. In particular, the chapter considers how best to avoid two extremes: creating unnecessary conflicts between science and Scripture, and slavishly accommodating Scripture to the latest scientific fads. The overarching goal must be to see Christ in the Scripture and to so read it that the saving message of the Gospel is always at the center.

Finally, the last chapter offers some guidance and practical applications and promotes further discussion for several vocational groups. How should Christian students of science respond to ideas that create challenges for their faith? How might Christian teachers present controversial ideas in the most constructive fashion? What factors may help Christian scientific investigators themselves to retain a strong sense of vocation and to integrate their faith with their work? And how should non-scientific Christian laity respond to the many claims made on behalf of science, some of which go far beyond what the data are saying? In each case, examples are given that may provide models for subsequent discussion. Let us pray that the ensuing conversations aid all of us in seeing that it is in Christ that all things hold together.

Chapter I

Theological Foundations

1. Introduction

Science and Christian Theology both present themselves as sources of knowledge. Fundamentally, questions about knowledge—epistemological questions[29]— are questions of authority. Do we think that observation and reason are the most authoritative sources for reliable belief? Or do we accept that Scripture is the final word? If science appears to conflict with the Bible, how do we adjudicate the dispute? To answer these questions, we must first consider the authority of Scripture and the proper role of reason, including scientific reason,[30] for a Christian believer (section 2). Next, a closely related question concerns the best way to relate nature and the Bible. Going back at least as far as Augustine (354–430), it has been common for theologians to say that God has revealed Himself in two books, the book of God's Word (Scripture, or special revelation), and the book of nature (creation, or general revelation).[31] Are these two sources equally authoritative or does one source take precedence over the other? If the latter, does that allow due respect for the contributions of the subordinate source? It is important to think through how the two books interrelate (section 3).

Once these foundational epistemological issues have been addressed, we can consider their implications for the life of the Christian scientist, for the relationship between Christianity and culture, for the nature of creation, and for the nature of humanity. What does it mean to see science as a vocation, and not merely a profession (section 4)? If we consider the various models

---

[29] Epistemology means "theory of knowledge." It is both an established branch of philosophy and a critical element of the methodology of many disciplines, including science and theology. Both of the latter disciplines make knowledge claims and address the question, "How can we know?"

[30] Scientific reason adds to standard reason principles of empirical investigation, such as the inductive method and procedures for testing scientific theories against the data and each other.

[31] Rebutting the Manicheans and arguing that nature was essentially good despite its fallen condition, Augustine said "But had you begun with looking on the book of nature as the production of the Creator of all ... you would not have been led into these impious follies and blasphemous fancies with which, in your ignorance of what evil really is, you heap all evils upon God" (*Contra Faustum Manichaeum* 32.20 in *Nicene and Post-Nicene Fathers*, series I, Vol. 4, ed. Philip Schaff [Grand Rapids: Christian Classics Ethereal Library], 583, available at: http://www.ccel.org/ccel/schaff/npnf104.pdf). Origen had anticipated this view by maintaining that the natural world is full of symbols, suggesting a text that might be read. See Peter Harrison, "The Bible and the Emergence of Modern Science," *Science and Christian Belief* 18:2 (2006): 115–132, 118, available at: https://www.scienceandchristianbelief.org/articles/Harrison-article-18-2.pdf.

Christians have used to negotiate culture, what are their implications for the intersection of faith and science, and which of these models is most congenial to a Lutheran understanding (section 5)? And what difference does it make to science if we see nature, and ourselves, as creations, not accidents (section 6 and 7)? Finally, we will see how Christian theology, rather than being a superstitious relic of our pre-scientific past, provides a strong foundation and motivation for modern science (section 8).

2. The authority of Scripture and the proper role of reason

As society moves in post-Christian directions, we see an increasing number of books on science and religion which assume without argument that science is the highest authority. While some of these works are overtly antagonistic to revealed religion,[32] it is common even among the friendlier ones to assume that science can correct Scripture. For example, in a recent work on the neuroscience of religious experience, Andrew Newberg and Mark Waldman reject biblical Christianity in favor of a more inclusive, Unitarian spirituality. They claim that it is a matter of pragmatic survival that our belief in God should progress:

> [I]f you cannot change your image of God, you may have trouble tolerating people who hold different images of God, and that may threaten our planet's survival.... if you cling to your childhood perceptions, you will limit your perception of the truth. This is the drawback to any religion that insists upon a literal, biblical image of God.[33]

The controlling idea for the New Atheist or opponents of biblical Christianity is that what we should believe about God is defined by what science has revealed as the best way for humans to get along in this world. The assumption here and in many similar works is that the human brain has generated various pictures of God, and the important question is to determine which picture is most useful on therapeutic and sociological grounds. The idea that God might authoritatively reveal the truth of Himself to us from above is rejected in favor of a pragmatic theology from below, which does not see religion as a matter of truth at all.

---

[32] Some obvious examples would be the works of the New Atheists, such as: Richard Dawkins, *The God Delusion* (New York: Houghton Mifflin, 2006) and *The Magic of Reality* (New York: The Free Press, 2011); Daniel Dennett, *Breaking the Spell: Religion as a Natural Phenomenon* (New York: Penguin, 2007); Steven Pinker, *The Better Angels of our Nature: Why Violence Has Declined* (New York: Viking Penguin, 2011); and Lawrence Krauss, *A Universe from Nothing: Why There Is Something Rather than Nothing* (New York: The Free Press, 2012).

[33] Andrew Newberg and Mark Waldman, *How God Changes the Brain* (New York: Ballantine Books, 2009), 103–104.

In response to this, it is important to gain a correct understanding of the authority of Scripture and of the proper role of reason. Lutheran theology is clear that the Scripture is the inspired,[34] infallible Word of God,[35] and as such it is our highest authority and most reliable criterion for knowledge. Due to its divine source, Scripture is in a quite different category from the perspective of any human faculty, including our senses and reason. These faculties at best tell us how the spatio-temporal world most likely operates, from a finite, creaturely perspective. But we are severely limited by a number of factors.

First, we live at particular locations in space and time and our attempts to reconstruct the past and to anticipate the future are fraught with uncertainty because of our limited access to data and the need to make assumptions which could be false (such as the assumption that processes observed in the present operated in the same way in the remote past, and will continue to do so in the future).[36] Second, although science has been spectacularly successful in positing mechanisms and laws behind the world of appearances, there is no warrant for supposing this gives us the final answer as to how the world really is in itself. Given our vantage point, it seems the best we can hope for is to discover contingent patterns and regularities: to say that these are absolute, necessary laws of nature on a par with the Law of God goes far beyond what the data justify.[37] After all, the entire cosmos is temporary and in constant flux; it is not a place of timeless truth. Third, as Francis Bacon (1561–1626) taught us, even with the data we have, we are prone to bias—to "idols of the mind"— in our interpretation of those data.[38] A major flaw in Bacon's account, however, is that he supposed we could cleanse ourselves from bias, so as to perform a "true induction" from the data alone. This conflicts with the fact that sin affects not only our religious and moral faculties, but also our reason. Our sinful desire for godlike knowledge and mastery of reality

---

[34] 2 Timothy 3:16; 2 Peter 1:19.

[35] For an explanation of the meanings of "inspired" and "infallible" as understood by the Lutheran Church Missouri—Synod, see: "A Statement of Scriptural and Confessional Principles, IV Holy Scripture," available at: http://www.lcms.org/doctrine/scripturalprinciples#IV.

[36] In philosophy, this is related to Hume's "problem of induction." David Hume showed that there is no way to give a logical justification for our inductive expectation that the future will resemble the past, because any principle we use (such as "nature is uniform") assumes that resemblance, making the argument circular.

[37] In fact, it conflicts with recent science itself to say this, as most scientists accept that the universe could have had quite different laws (the laws of nature are contingent on the "fine tuning" of the universe).

[38] See Francis Bacon, *The New Organon*, ed. by Lisa Jardine and Michael Silverthorne (New York: Cambridge University Press, 2000), Bk I. Bacon distinguished: "idols of the tribe," which afflict all human beings, e.g., reading non-existent order into coincidences; "idols of the cave," which afflict individuals, e.g., the influence of a mentor; "idols of the market place," or confusions caused by language, e.g., treating cold as a real thing; and "idols of the theatre" or mistaken rules of demonstration, e.g., the Aristotelian idea that determining what an object must do by intuiting its essence made it unnecessary to determine empirically if that object does behave in that way.

makes us expect more from science than it can or should give: we want the final answers and final control to lie in the works of our own minds.[39] Another name for this is idolatry, which makes us deny our creaturely dependence on God, our inability to cure our sinful condition, and our need for a Savior.

Thus, as finite, fallen creatures, our assumption should be that human thought constructions are penultimate, incomplete and prone to error both in detail and in their systematic orientation and design. That does not mean we should give up on using reason or doing science, however. Reason is a valuable gift, but its proper function is that of a servant oriented to the service of neighbor, rather than that of a usurping judge that aims to correct or to supplant God. Luther made this clear in his important distinction between the right and wrong use of reason when approaching God's Word.[40] The wrong use of reason—the "magisterial use"—allows human reason to judge which aspects of God's Word are (or are not) acceptable. This means that the finite, contingent and fallible works of the human mind are used to evaluate the revelation of an infinite, necessary, and infallible God, which exaggerates the certainty of science and undermines confidence in God's Word. The right use of reason—the "ministerial use"— is that of a servant to revelation. Following Anselm (1033–1109), reason may be used to aid a *faith seeking understanding* (*fides quarens intellectum*), for example, when systematic theology explores the consequences of Scripture for various doctrines. It may also be used *to defend the faith* (Christian apologetics), and to *apply the faith* in the Christian life (Christian ethics). In the latter case, it may help to disclose the best, specific means of serving a neighbor, concerning which Scripture is often silent. Scripture contains no books of plumbing or automotive repair: it exhorts us to love our neighbor as ourselves, but leaves the techniques to human ingenuity.

Science is a spectacular manifestation of human reason. But for all its success and power, still science is rightly understood as a servant. It has a very important role, but a limited one. Science is not authorized to stand as an arbiter over God and His Word, and it makes no contribution to our salvation. But it is a wonderful gift for Christian living in this world. As a minister that serves our faith, science vastly increases our ability to meet our neighbor's temporal needs. So we should neither exalt science as a surrogate religion,

---

[39] In this regard, Bacon himself is frequently criticized for his dictum "knowledge is power," which expressed his belief that a major motivation for science is to gain control of the natural world. While Bacon claimed that this was for "the relief of man's estate," the temptation of this power is that it provides the illusion that we are not creatures dependent on God's common and salvific grace, but masters of our own destiny. For C. S. Lewis, this was the primary temptation behind the tower of Babel (Gen. 11) and its modern equivalent: a "scientocracy" in which human technology replaces God as our Provider and Savior. For an incisive, recent exploration of this theme, see John G. West, *The Magician's Twin: C. S. Lewis on Science, Scientism, and Society* (Seattle: Discovery Institute Press, 2012).

[40] For an excellent discussion of Luther's views on the proper role of reason in the spiritual and earthly realms, see Steven A. Hein, "Reason and the Two Kingdoms: An Essay in Luther's Thought," *The Springfielder* 36:2 (September 1972), available on-line at: http://www.ctsfw.net/media/pdfs/heinreasontwokingdoms.pdf.

which dispenses with the need for revelation, nor despise it on account of its potential for misuse.[41] Rather, the proper approach is a middle way, in which science is an instrument that serves our scripturally revealed purpose to love one another, as Christ has loved us.

3. The proper relationship between God's "two books"

It might seem that this settles the question of how to read God's "two books," the book of Scripture (God's Word) and the book of nature (God's works). Yet while Scripture is the supreme source and norm for knowledge, the interplay between scientific and scriptural knowledge is a subtle matter. One of the main reasons for this is the human tendency to impose meanings on a text that are not there, which can happen both with the scriptural and the natural text. It is easy to do *eisegesis* (where the interpreter expresses his or her own preferred ideas, though they do not derive from the text itself), when we are called to do *exegesis* (to draw out the meaning that really resides in the text). In particular, if we wrongly assume that Scripture is speaking in the terms of a scientific theory when it is not, or if we assume that nature can only be understood through that theory, we may easily construct a false conflict between the two books.

A famous example of this is the alleged contradiction between modern science and Joshua 10:12–13, which describes a day when the sun stood still. If we suppose this text to be expressing a scientific theory in astronomy, it is easy to suppose that Scripture is committed to the geocentric paradigm, according to which the sun is one of many planets going round a stationary Earth. So the sun "standing still" means that it became still like the Earth. The problem is that we now have excellent reason to reject the geocentric paradigm in favor of a heliocentric one, in which the Earth is one of many planets going around the Sun. Although Scripture is our supreme standard, it would be improperly dogmatic to insist that human science is simply wrong before considering whether our interpretation of Scripture was required by the text. The Bible is a collection of inspired, infallible writings, yet God inspires human writers to convey His message in humanly comprehensible terms. And throughout the Scripture we see God communicating to us in the terms of common-sense appearances.

For example, we are told eight times in Matthew's gospel that the kingdom of Heaven is *like* various familiar things accessible to the senses, such as a mustard seed, leaven and treasure. Using this approach, the Joshua text simply says that from an earthbound perspective the sun appeared to be still (which is remarkable enough), which does not imply that the Earth

---

[41] The principle here is *abusus non tollit usum* (abuse does remove proper use). Thus, for example, the fact that wine may be abused does not remove its proper use in Holy Communion.

is absolutely stationary and does not involve commitment to a particular astronomical theory. It then becomes clear that the apparent conflict between science and Scripture was generated by reading scientific claims into Scripture that were simply not there.

This example suggests that we must proceed with caution when putting Scripture and nature side by side. Living after the scientific revolution, it is difficult for us to see nature without already conceiving of it in scientific terms. This poses several dangers for our proper reading of Scripture. One of these is that whenever Scripture speaks about a natural topic, we naturally suppose it is speaking in scientific terms. We then complain, for example, that the mustard seed is not "the smallest of all seeds" (Mt. 13:32) or that grains of wheat do not "die" when buried in the ground (John 12:24; 1 Cor. 15:36), when it is clear that we are being presented with potent images of faith and our baptism into the death and resurrection of Christ. Thus, before even raising the question of whether science is relevant to a scriptural text, we must first ask: what is the primary message of the text? That primary message is a helpful guide to discerning the genre of the text. If the primary message of the preceding passages is about how man is saved, and the truth is a spiritual and theological one expressed in the images understood by a particular audience not versed in modern science, it is both gratuitous and anachronistic to impose a wooden interpretation based on contemporary science, as if the principal purpose had been to offer advice in modern agronomy (these matters are taken up at greater length in chapter 4).

But another problem is that in our scientific age, an unexamined presumption of scientism (the view that science is the only source of knowledge) can deaden our sensibilities to deeper truths God intends to communicate through nature, simply because we lack a scientific framework for making sense of them. This was one of C. S. Lewis's concerns in his great work on the transition from the medieval to the modern world, *The Discarded Image*.[42] Lewis was well aware that the Aristotelian-Ptolemaic model of the seven planets was false as science, but he rightly lamented that in rejecting that model, modern science also encouraged the rejection of some theological truths that model had been used to express. Lewis pointed out that, as developed by medieval thinkers who suggested that each planet was guided by an angelic intelligence, this model beautifully expressed the truth of God's universal, immanent presence in the world. However, after Newton—himself a religious believer—it became easy to think that space was just a dark, silent void (Newton had thought of space as simply a vacuum, something more recent science has rejected[43]). By unconsciously transferring this cosmological model into the realm of theology, it is much easier for modern people to

---

[42] C. S. Lewis, *The Discarded Image* (New York: Cambridge University Press, 1994).

[43] According to the latest cosmological theories, "empty" space is actually filled with dark matter and dark energy.

be deists, who accept God's existence as a transcendent being, but who deny His providential, immanent presence within the cosmos and in each of our lives. [44]

By contrast, Scripture tells us that God is so intimately concerned with each one us, that even the hairs of our head are numbered (Matt. 10:30). Furthermore, nature is not a silent void but an active means of communication between God and man:

> The heavens declare the glory of God,
>> and the sky above proclaims his handiwork.
> Day to day pours out speech,
>> and night to night reveals knowledge. (Ps. 19:1–2)

We should not assume that this is a thesis of modern, scientific, information theory, demanding that we uncover a hidden system of transmitting data to us in rocks, animals and plants! Rather, the natural world was not only created by God's Word, but is still governed by it. His Word, His *logos*, is inscribed in nature and speaks to us of God's glorious design and providence. So not only should we resist imposing alien scientific interpretations on Scripture, we should also see that science is not the *only* way of understanding nature. Scripture opens our mind to the natural world as a source of spiritual and theological knowledge: it speaks of God, His attributes and His works, and it testifies to a God whose involvement in this world is ubiquitous and ongoing.

At the same time, it is possible to impose scriptural and theological truths on science in inappropriate ways. For example, as Peter Harrison points out, the scholastic approach to both science and Scripture emphasized allegorical over literal interpretations.[45] Not only did this mean that the plain meaning of Scripture was sometimes obscured by endless speculations about secondary, symbolic meanings, but it also meant that Scripture was sometimes inappropriately imposed on science in order to see nature as a storehouse of moral and theological lessons for mankind. A well-known example of this is the ancient Christian symbolism of the pelican which, in Christlike fashion, wounds its own breast to feed its young with its blood. As a poetic image this is poignant and powerful, but pelicans do not in fact do this.[46] It is important to see that the main goal of science is to offer accurate, testable descriptions

---

[44] Evidence for this is found in the survey of American teen religiosity reported in Smith and Denton, *Soul Searching*. Smith and Denton say that a common view held by members of a variety of religious groups (both Christian and non-Christian) is that the religious life is about being good (moralism), feeling good (therapy), and a distant God who is there if needed but otherwise stays uninvolved in our lives (deism). For more on the origin of moralistic therapeutic deism, see chapter 2 of this report.

[45] Peter Harrison, *The Bible, Protestantism, and the Rise of Natural Science* (New York: Cambridge University Press, 1998).

[46] This poetic image continues to be used on occasion in Christian hymnody. See *Lutheran Service Book* (St. Louis: Concordia Publishing House, 2006), 640, v. 3.

and explanation. The statements of science do not claim to have moral or religious significance, and one is forsaking science proper when one adds a value-laden interpretation to them (even though that interpretation may be philosophically or theologically sound). It is important, therefore, to distinguish carefully what science as science can tell us from further conclusions we may draw with the aid of additional, non-scientific assumptions. Science alone cannot tell us that nature is a medium of God's communication to mankind. But then, we should never have supposed that science is the only way of knowing in the first place.

A second problem, which reflects the influence of scientism on our thinking, is that modern Christians are tempted to use science as a way of proving Scripture. This is an odd approach, given the relative status of science in relation to Scripture. Scripture is the eternal, infallible revelation of a perfect Being uncontaminated with sin and unlimited by spatio-temporal location. Yet the finite and fallible findings of human reason are thought necessary to establish the authority of God's Word! To be sure, in an apologetic context, when dealing with someone who does not accept Scripture as God's Word, it is very helpful to provide independent, scientific evidence in favor of its major claims. The problem arises, however, when a particular scientific theory or finding is used as a final proof of a scriptural text. Science by its nature is a fallible enterprise, and its theories and even its most basic assertions are frequently revised. For centuries, nothing seemed more obvious than that the Earth is stationary, that weight and time are constants, that light travels in straight lines, and that nature makes no jumps; yet the advances of Copernicus, Newton, Einstein and quantum theory have shown that every one of these ideas is mistaken. Pluto, discovered in 1930, survived as a "planet" only until 2006, when scientists reclassified the heavenly body as a "dwarf planet," although the decision remains controversial and may be reversed.[47] It is unwise to rely on fallible conjectures that may tomorrow be consigned to the dustbin of science, in order to give the final seal of veracity on Scripture's claims.

To summarize this discussion, rather than relying on a simplistic algorithm for relating God's two books (such as NOMA,[48] with its stark separation between God's Word and God's work), it is helpful to keep in mind several principles about Scripture, science, and their interrelationship:

1. Scripture, not science, is God's Word. It is inspired and infallible, even as its source is a perfect Being unaffected by sin or finitude.

---

[47] For a recent discussion, see Doyle Rice, "Wait, what? Pluto a planet again?" *USA Today*, October 2, 2014, available at: http://www.usatoday.com/story/tech/2014/10/02/pluto-planet-solar-system/16578959/.

[48] On NOMA, or, "nonoverlapping magisteria," see Introduction, 7. The concept is given further consideration in chapter 3.

2. Yet, the Scripture speaks through its inspired human writers, and generally reflects the way the world ordinarily appears in their experience. It should not be assumed that Scripture advocates a particular scientific theory, or that all of its claims about particulars are presented in a scientific manner.

3. Science is not the only source of knowledge about nature. As science is currently practiced, it aims at a literal, value-free description and explanation of nature, and is not able to account for deeper meanings. Scripture tells us of a natural revelation in which God, our Creator, speaks to us through the medium of the natural world to reveal His orderly design and providential care of His creation (Ps. 19:1–2). This does not have to be understood as a scientific account, but is an independent source of knowledge in its own right.

4. Scriptural and theological interpretations of nature, while they are legitimate and valuable, should not be confused with science itself. Science can provide knowledge about the "what" and "how" of nature, but only Christian theology—revealed partially in nature and with full clarity and authority in Scripture—can explain the "why" of nature and help us to behold God with the majesty and awe that His work deserves. This is precisely why a rich theology of nature should complement natural science.

5. For the purpose of Christian apologetics, scientific evidence may be used in support of scriptural claims (about nature or all theology), but due to the fallible nature of science, it is incapable of providing certainty of proof. Rather, Scripture is self-authenticating.

In applying these principles, we are pointed toward the primary purposes of Scripture and science. As John's Gospel tells us, God's Word is "written so that you may believe that Jesus is the Christ, the Son of God, and that by believing you may have life in his name" (John 20:31). So our central focus in reading Scripture must be on what Scripture tells about the nature and work of Christ and on our living relationship with Him. That means that the scientific implications of scriptural statements should generally be given only secondary attention, and may often be irrelevant to the intended sense of the text. Likewise, the primary purpose of science is to tell us how nature appears to be working. Speculations about the meaning and value of this working should be viewed as secondary layers of philosophical and theological interpretation, not as part of science proper. While NOMA suggests (at least in theory) that there is no overlap between science and theology, it is apparent that is not the case. There is overlap—often significant overlap. And, where they overlap, Christian theology asserts that Scripture, not science, has final authority. Nevertheless, it is critical to see that the overlap is partial, not complete. Both science and theology have important roles. In Lutheran terms, both the vocations of the scientist and the theologian are honorable and godly. Neither replaces the other. Both are ultimately intended for the glory of God and the well-being of His creatures—most especially humankind, the crown of His creation.

4. The doctrine of vocation

When God tells us to love and serve our neighbor, the ways that we fulfill this command are defined by our various vocations.[49] A vocation is a calling from God to serve our neighbor where He has placed us using the gifts He has provided. Science itself should not be a pursuit devised by human beings to satisfy our own curiosity or gratify our desire for power and control. It reflects our primary call to be stewards of the earth, which requires us to use reason to understand the nature and operation of our natural environment, so that we can utilize its potential to develop culture[50] and preserve its resources for posterity. All vocations are bound by God's law, and so the scientific vocation is not a license to exploit the world but involves duties, responsibilities and other moral boundaries. The world is not a disposable asset, but a trust which we are to husband for the good of present and future generations of people, all of whom are our neighbors.

It is important to understand the contrast between this understanding of science and the one prevalent today, that science is a "profession." Vocation and profession are not the same thing. To see the difference, it is helpful to contrast the self-understanding of scientists at the birth of modern science with the one which has become dominant since the 19th century. Some of the greatest scientists of the modern scientific revolution in the 16th and 17th centuries were Christians. They were greatly interested in theology, and they wanted a way to conceive of their scientific work as a God-pleasing activity. Before the Reformation, "vocation" was a term reserved for specifically ecclesial offices, such as priest, monk, or nun. However, Luther emphasized the priesthood of all believers (1 Pet. 2:9), which implied that ordinary, earthly work (in the home, in society, and the workplace) was God-pleasing. Combining this insight with the idea that nature is God's other book, several leading scientists, including Johannes Kepler (1571–1630) and Robert Boyle (1627–1691), came to see themselves as priests in the book of nature.[51] So

---

[49] For an accessible exposition of the doctrine of vocation as a theology of Christian living, see Gene Edward Veith, *God at Work: Your Christian Vocation in All of Life*, Redesign Edition (Wheaton, IL: Crossway Books, 2011). For a superb exposition of the doctrine as developed by Luther, see Gustaf Wingren's masterpiece, *Luther on Vocation* (Eugene, OR: Wipf and Stock, 2004). For an approach oriented to Bible study, see Angus Menuge, "Vocation," in ed. Edward Engelbrecht, *The Lutheran Difference* (St. Louis: Concordia Publishing House, 2010).

[50] A succinct definition of "culture" as the term is used in this report is "what humans do to nature to serve their own purposes."

[51] See Peter Harrison, "Priests of the Most High God, with Respect to the Book of Nature," in ed. Angus Menuge, *Reading God's World: The Scientific Vocation* (St. Louis: Concordia Publishing House, 2004), 59–84.

influential was this paradigm for several centuries that workers in this area were often described as natural theologians.

Indeed, the word "scientist" is a new one, not entering the lexicon until 1834,[52] and it signified a momentous change in the way science was conceived:

> The success of this new designation is not merely a semantic curiosity because it was largely a reflection of the general growth of distinct professions during this period. More importantly, the appearance of the term *scientist* signaled the end of that typically eighteenth- and nineteenth-century phenomenon of the priest-naturalist. Over the course of the nineteenth century deliberate moves were afoot to elevate the status of the natural sciences .... This could only take place, many believed, if the social powers of the priesthood were challenged and the domination of the university curriculum by theology and the humanities brought to an end .... Henceforth, it is the scientist who is the authoritative purveyor of true and useful knowledge.[53]

The key to the reconceiving of science as a profession, rather than a priestly vocation, is the assertion that science is independent of the church. The scientist is no longer seen as a priest (in the broad sense) who happens to like laboratories or the great outdoors. Instead, the scientist is someone who follows the methods and procedures prescribed by professional bodies independent of the church—which generally means a group of qualified individuals directing the trajectory of scientific research or practice.

On the one hand, it is true that modern science does not require a person to be a Christian: it recognizes a general human condition, according to which the procedures and results of science must be accessible to any competent investigator, regardless of ideological or religious persuasion. So it is fair to say that practicing science does not require one to see science *as* a vocation. But on the other hand, those scientists who are Christian lose a great deal when they are trained to see their work merely as a profession. Indeed, as Nancy Pearcey has argued, these scientists often experience considerable internal conflict, because they do not see how to relate their life as a Christian with their work as a scientist.[54]

The difference this makes is that vocation provides a framework of religious and moral meaning for scientific work which is severely truncated in

---

[52] The term was coined by William Whewell (1794–1866).

[53] Harrison, "Priests of the Most High God," 78.

[54] See Nancy Pearcey, "How Science Became a Christian Vocation," in ed. Angus Menuge, *Reading God's World: The Scientific Vocation* (St. Louis: Concordia Publishing House, 2004), 23–57 and her *Total Truth* (Wheaton, IL: Crossway Books, 2004).

the concept of a profession. Professional standards of scientific conduct say nothing about being called by God to be a steward of His creation, or about our obligation to love and serve our neighbor through all that we do.[55] On this understanding, while Christian scientists may benefit from their faith in private, they may see no meaningful way to relate their faith to their public work. A recurrent problem is that while professional codes of ethics may express the consensus on "best practice," they do not reflect a biblical understanding of morality, especially as it bears on the dignity and value of all life. But the disconnect is also found in the inability of some scientists to integrate their findings with a Christian worldview. To cite one of Pearcey's starkest examples, one Christian quantum physicist, when asked how he related his faith to his work, said merely that quantum mechanics is like auto-mechanics, and had *no* connection with his faith.[56] Had this scientist thought through the implications of the doctrine of vocation, he might have realized that faith is relevant to both auto-mechanics and quantum mechanics. Both are ways of glorifying God by unveiling the ordering principles God built into nature and by serving our neighbor through discovering nature's secrets and developing beneficial technology.[57]

Not only does the idea of vocation invest science with considerably more meaning than the secularized notion of a profession, it also provides important guidance and boundaries for scientific work. If the goal is to love and serve one's neighbor then the scientist should not do certain things. He or she should not merely pursue a popular form of technology because it will make money or make the scientist famous. These outcomes as such are not wrong, but they should be the result of developing a product which serves human welfare, not the primary motivation for doing science. A great example of someone whose Christian values informed and guided his science is Robert Boyle. After studying theology and ethics, Boyle went into science partly to discover inexpensive, chemical remedies for the ailments of the poor.[58] This moral motivation for doing science is a powerful way of finding meaning in scientific work.

Likewise, some forms of scientific experimentation will be off-limits because they are unethical. If they directly involve, or indirectly cause, avoidable harm to people, the faithful scientist should think hard about whether

---

[55] Originally, the "Hippocratic Oath," which physicians swore to uphold, contained a prayer and forbade practices which would harm patients. The various oaths now used by many medical schools typically omit any prayer and also omit certain practices from the list of proscribed procedures (most notably abortion).

[56] Pearcey, "How Science Became a Christian Vocation," 27.

[57] Admittedly, quite a bit of theoretical quantum mechanics might seem remote to serving our neighbor's needs, but in fact it lies behind such incredibly useful technological innovations as the laser.

[58] See Edward B. Davis, "Science As Christian Vocation," in ed. Angus Menuge, *Reading God's World: The Scientific Vocation* (St. Louis: Concordia Publishing House, 2004), 189–210.

one can in good conscience participate in the research and even about whether it should be openly opposed. Human beings are specially made in the image of God. While we are authorized, within limits, to shape the non-human environment to serve our needs, we should not attempt to "flatten" creation, so that other human beings are also treated merely as natural resources. As the great philosopher Immanuel Kant (1724–1804) said in his ethical writings, we should never treat other persons as a means to an end but always as ends in themselves.[59] What he meant was that persons are not merely things which exist to be used for various purposes. Persons have value in themselves. It is a violation of the dignity of persons for us to use them merely as a collection of experimental resources to serve our purposes, as if we were persons but they were not.

5. Christianity and culture

When negotiating the intersection between faith and science, a theological assumption that plays a large role in how these realms are understood to relate to each other concerns the proper way for the Christian to approach culture. Although it can be criticized, the classic typology for relating Christianity and culture developed by H. Richard Niebuhr (1894–1962) is helpful in explaining the different approaches of various theological traditions.[60]

Niebuhr distinguishes two one-dimensional models and three two-dimensional models. The one-dimensional models involve the radical extremes of rejecting culture for Christ ("Christ against culture") or affirming culture for Christ ("Christ of culture"). The two-dimensional models emphasize that God is King of all things and that He rules in two ways, through two "kingdoms." He rules in our hearts through the spiritual kingdom of grace through faith. But He also rules the earthly kingdom through various orders He has instituted to maintain order and to preserve His creation.

a. The one-dimensional models

The Christ against culture paradigm, exemplified by Leo Tolstoy (1828–1910) and the Mennonites, sees the Christian's calling as one of following Christ directly in all of life. Thus obligations to the state (taxes, oaths of allegiance) may be seen as violations of the first commandment. Since Christ

---

[59] This is the second formulation of his celebrated "categorical imperative," which attempts to explicate the rational basis for the golden rule: do unto others as you would have them do to you. The first formulation of the categorical imperative says: so act that you can will your action to be a universal law for all people. It attempts to short circuit the person who wants to do a wrong that they rely on others not doing, such as burglary.

[60] H. Richard Niebuhr, *Christ and Culture* (New York: Harper & Row, 1956). For a critical evaluation of this work see, for example, ed. Angus Menuge, *Christ and Culture in Dialogue* (St. Louis: Concordia Publishing House, 1999) and D. A. Carson, *Christ and Culture Revisited* (Grand Rapids: Eerdmans, 2012). See also the appendices Z, AA, and BB in Charles Manske and Daniel Harmelink, *World Religions Today* (Irvine, CA: Institute of World Religions, 1996) for a helpful two-page outline and chart illustrating Niebuhr's model.

tells us to love our enemy and turn the other cheek, the Christian should not be a soldier. Fundamentally, the Christ Against Culture view is inadequate because Jesus himself recognizes a legitimate role for temporal authority: we are to render unto Caesar what is Caesar's (Matt. 22:21). Even Pilate has some authority over Christ in His human nature, because that authority was given to him from above (John 19:11). Likewise, Paul explains that the governing authorities are instituted by God and so one cannot simply set the claims of God against the claims of the state (Rom. 13). It is only if government abuses its office and commands the Christian to do what is directly contrary to the Law of God that we must obey God rather than men (Acts 5:29).

Examples of the Christ of culture model include both Modernist and Postmodernist Christianity. Modernizers, like Rudolf Bultmann (1884–1976), sought to square Christian teaching with a worldview dominated by scientific materialism. Thus, they rejected literal miracles in favor of existential interpretations in the life of the Christian (e. g., people do not really rise from the dead, but you will experience a new "life" within you, etc.). Postmodernizers (including currents within the "emergent church") have likewise sought to understand the Christian claim not as objective truth for all mankind but as the perspective of a particular community of language users.[61] More generally, much of mainline Protestantism is dominated by the idea that the culture sets the agenda for the church, and that one should carefully study the dominant or "best" cultural trends to discern the wisest course for Christians to take.

While cultural sensitivity and understanding are valuable for Christian evangelists and apologists, the basic problem for the Christ of Culture view is that even the best of culture is still infected with human sin. To follow culture when it conflicts with loyalty to Christ is selling out the faith to seek honor among men (Matt. 6:2; Gal. 1:10). Likewise, to reject miracles foundational to the faith or to propose a new gospel that is more "relevant" is nullifying the Word of God for the sake of human tradition (Matt. 15:6). It is a denial that the only true Gospel is the one from God (John 14:6, Acts 4:12, Gal. 1:6–9). In practice, this view tends to promote a cultural idolatry that buries the transcendent Gospel in a barrage of manmade agendas which disingenuously appropriate Christian vocabulary: the result may have the form of godliness, but it denies its true power (2 Tim. 3:5).[62]

Both of the one-dimensional models, therefore, are too simple to capture a proper understanding of the Christian's relationship to culture. Temporal

---

[61] For a balanced presentation and effective critique of several major theses of the emergent church movement, see R. Scott Smith, *Truth and the New Kind of Christian: The Emerging Effects of Postmodernism in the Church* (Wheaton, IL: Crossway Books, 2007).

[62] One of the greatest of the 20th century critics of such theological liberalism was J. Gresham Machen (1881–1937), who opposed the increasing compromise of God's Word in the Northern Presbyterian Church (now PCUSA). See *Christianity and Liberalism* (Grand Rapids: Eerdmans, 2009; first published in 1923).

authority has its place, as it is instituted by God, but slavish capitulation to culture is an abandonment of the Gospel. The two-dimensional models therefore try to hold the concerns of legitimate temporal authority (the earthly government) and allegiance to Christ (the spiritual government) in proper balance.

b. The two-dimensional models

The disagreement between theological traditions that accept the two kingdoms idea[63] centers on the relation between the kingdoms. Classical Catholic theology proposed a synthesis of the spiritual and earthly kingdoms ("Christ above culture") where the spiritual kingdom governs the earthly kingdom. Thus for Thomas Aquinas (1225–1274), there is a sharp distinction between the natural (temporal, earthly) ends of man, governed by the cardinal virtues (courage, justice, temperance and prudence), which are available to all people regardless of faith, and the supernatural (eternal, heavenly) ends of man, governed by the theological virtues (faith, hope, and charity), available to the Christian only through grace. What the Fall into sin did in this view was to sever humanity's connection to its supernatural ends, while leaving the ability to pursue natural ends basically intact. Thus redemption is a matter of restoring the supernatural ends (grace completing nature) in the individual Christian. Likewise, in a Christian society (such as the theocracies of medieval Christendom), ecclesial government (directed at our supernatural ends) completes earthly government (directed at our natural ends).

By contrast, in the Reformed tradition ("Christ the transformer of culture"), both the severity of the Fall and the scope of redemption are given a more dramatic understanding. The Reformed combine a deep pessimism about fallen man with a profound optimism about the implications of redemption. The Fall does not merely mean that humanity lost its orientation to supernatural ends. It means "total depravity": we are made enemies of God, and all of our faculties are turned away from God. Not only are individuals turned inward and regard themselves as gods, cultural institutions likewise assert their independence of God and glorify their own works in idolatrous rebellion. In this context, nothing but a complete transformation of the natural man can help. Grace does not complete nature; it fundamentally restructures and reorients it, yielding new life in Christ. The transformationist thinks that it is not only individuals, but cultures, that can be redeemed. So there is an emphasis on reclaiming the culture for Christ, supported by means and strategies such as Christian bookstores, Christian movies, and Christianized approaches to art, history, literature, government, and science.

The Lutheran perspective (typified by Niebuhr as "Christ and culture in paradox") agrees with the Reformed position that sin is a condition of total depravity, but disagrees that Christians should aim to redeem culture.

---

[63] See fn 23 for a succinct definition of "the two kingdoms."

30

Lutherans do believe that cultures can be changed for the better as Christians carry out their vocation in the world. But they believe that such change is temporary at best, and that we should simply aim to do the best that we can for the people we are able to help and with the gifts that God has provided. While individual Christians can exert an important influence in the political sphere, it does not make sense to seek to Christianize government because God's left-hand kingdom is not a place of abiding hope (Ps. 146:3). The unique and primary vocation of the church (which bears the Word) is to proclaim the Gospel in truth and purity and to rightly administer the sacraments. The vocation of government (which bears the Sword) is to restrain evil and uphold temporal order, thus allowing free passage for the Gospel. This means that government is susceptible to two main errors: it may wrongly present itself as an institution of salvation (as may happen in a state church), or it may wrongly use force to attempt the impossible task of coercing faith, failing to recognize that only God can create faith (Matt. 16:17; 1 Cor. 3:7). Earthly governments, therefore, provide a framework and context in which the Christian can serve his neighbor and witness to the Gospel, but our ultimate hope is in the kingdom that is *not* of this world (John 18:36).[64]

c. Applying these models to the intersection of faith and science

When these five models of Christianity and culture are applied to the intersection of faith and science, they yield strikingly different results which help us understand the wide disagreement between Christians on these matters, and also help to elucidate what is distinctive about a Lutheran approach to science.

A Christ against culture approach is liable to reject at least some of science on the grounds that its assumptions, aims, practices, and claims conflict with allegiance to Christ and His Word. At a moderate level, this might involve refusing to seriously evaluate or use particular statements, theories, and technologies. A more extreme reaction would be to reject the work and institutions of science altogether as idolatrous and godless diversions from Christ. Either way, it is likely that Christians with this perspective will feel uncomfortable about scientific work and this will disincline them to pursue science as a vocation. Surely, something has gone wrong here. The legitimacy of science is implicit in our original call to be stewards of God's world: how can we preserve this trust without knowing how nature operates? And if the scientific vocation aims merely to serve the neighbor and not to usurp Christ as Savior and Lord, there is no reason that it cannot be pursued by Christians.

A Christ of culture approach tends to reinterpret the Scriptures and Christian doctrines restlessly in light of the latest findings of science. Thus

---

[64] For a more extensive examination of the proper relationship between church and state, see the CTCR's report *Render Under Caesar... and Unto God: A Lutheran View of Church and State* (St. Louis: CPH, 1995), available at http://www.lcms.org/Document.fdoc?src=lcm&id=360.

the plausibility of miracles depends on whether they can be made to fit in current scientific theories, religious experience may be analyzed as something generated by "God genes" or "God spots" in the brain,[65] and God must create through the evolutionary process as presently conceived. We quickly see that this model lends itself to the magisterial use of reason. Science and Scripture exchange their actual status, disfiguring both: the Scriptures are viewed as science should be (fallible and limited) while the latest science is viewed as Scripture should be (ultimate authority). It also easily makes the anachronistic assumption that Scripture speaks in the same terms as current scientific theories, which may distort the true message of Scripture, set up a false conflict between science and Scripture and promote misguided attempts to "improve" Scripture. So far from saving Christianity by updating it, what this model actually does is to accord religious veneration to the findings of science (scientism) while deriding God's Word as an outmoded relic of a superstitious past.

The Christ above culture model offers an intellectually impressive response to the intersection of faith and reason. Seeing that God operates in both the natural world and the human heart, and believing that grace completes nature, it naturally encourages the idea that the best human science can be synthesized with the truths of Scripture. As Aquinas took Aristotle's cardinal virtues and synthesized them with the theological virtues, Aristotelian science was combined with Scripture. A more recent manifestation of the same approach is the attempt to combine the Christian faith with neo-Darwinian evolutionary theory.[66] The fatal flaw of this approach is the way in which it attempts to fuse the ultimate and the penultimate, the eternal and the contingent, the infallible and the fallible. Simply joining Christianity with the latest and greatest scientific theory is a bad idea because it creates the false sense that the authority of the Word rests on that theory. So when Aristotelian science was roundly rejected at the birth of modern science, it appeared that Christianity itself had been discredited. Likewise, an increasing number of scholars agree with eminent philosopher Thomas Nagel's assessment that the reductive materialism which lies behind the Neo-Darwinian paradigm is "ripe for displacement,"[67] as it offers no credible account of the origin of biological information, consciousness, and the norms of rationality and morality. Marrying Christianity with science is not only prone to producing widows, it creates inappropriate pressure to make Christian teachings "fit"

---

[65] For a survey and critique of such debunking accounts of religious experience, see Mario Beauregard and Denyse O'Leary, *The Spiritual Brain: A Neuroscientist's Case for the Existence of the Soul* (New York: HarperCollins, 2007).

[66] See, for example, Kenneth Miller, *Finding Darwin's God: A Scientist's Search for Common Ground Between God and Evolution* (New York: HarperCollins, 1999), and *Only a Theory: Evolution and the Battle for America's Soul* (New York: Viking Penguin, 2008).

[67] Thomas Nagel, *Mind and Cosmos: Why the Materialist Neo-Darwinian Conception of Nature Is Almost Certainly False* (New York: Oxford University Press, 2012), 12.

scientific findings or to impose Christian interpretations on scientific facts, thereby confusing the two realms. The result is often a curious mélange of science and theology which draws fire from both the best scientists and the best theologians.[68]

Niebuhr's fifth model ("Christ transforming culture") recognizes, to its credit, that there is likely to be a great deal of apparent conflict when the ideas of finite, fallen humans meet the transcendent Word of God. But rather than distancing itself from science, like the Christ against culture approach, in this view the solution is to transform and redeem science so that it honors Christ. In one way this is very helpful. Science is not a self-sufficient enterprise, but rests on frequently unexamined presuppositions. A transformation- ist, inspired by Paul's admonition to "destroy arguments and every lofty opinion raised against the knowledge of God," and to "take every thought captive to obey Christ" (2 Cor. 10:5), may skillfully expose in secular thought the presence of philosophical assumptions about the nature and purpose of science which are antagonistic to Christianity. For example, it may reveal the limitations of assuming "methodological naturalism," a rule of scientific procedure which asserts that scientists may infer only natural causes for every phenomena. This may be a perfectly reasonable rule of thumb in many areas of science, but when it is treated as an absolute criterion of knowledge it excludes not only miracles but also God's providential activity in all of nature.

However, just as transformationists may be tempted by the theocratic impulse to Christianize government, so they may also attempt to Christianize science once and for all. This makes the same mistake as the synthesis model. In Niebuhr's phrase, it "absolutizes the relative": it attempts to find ultimate, eternal, infallible truth in science which can only offer penultimate, temporal, fallible conjectures and models. This is, in effect, an epistemology of glory, one which tries to reach up and know God by reason. What is needed instead is an epistemology of the cross, which accepts the creaturely limitations of all our mental constructs and humbly receives illumination from above through faith in Christ and His Word.[69]

In contrast to these other paradigms, the "paradox" model, attributed by Niebuhr to Luther and Lutheranism, has several resources to develop a more wholesome relationship between faith and science. First, since it does not look to anything in this world as a source of final answers, it declines

---

[68] Arguably, a good example of this is the theistic evolution of Denis Alexander and Francis Collins, roundly criticized by both scientists and theologians in Norman Nevin, ed., *Should Christians Embrace Evolution? Biblical and Scientific Responses* (Philipsburg, NJ: P & R Publishing, 2011). The problem can also arise when studying the neuroscience associated with religious experience, as discussed above.

[69] For a brilliant discussion of the distinction between an "epistemology of glory" and an "epistemology of the cross," see Jeff Mallinson, "Epistemology of the Cross: A Lutheran Response to Philosophical Theisms," in Adam Francisco, Steven Mueller and Korey D. Maas, eds., *Theologia et Apologia: Essays in Reformation Theology and Its Defense Presented to Rod Rosenblatt* (Eugene, OR: Wipf and Stock, 2007).

scientism as offering what C. S. Lewis called "the sweet poison of the false infinite."[70] In other words, the paradox model recognizes that, like all human works, science cannot "save humanity" or "save the world." But, second, the paradox model affirms that science can indeed aid us in loving and serving our neighbor, so that Christians have good reason to explore and employ useful scientific theories and ideas, even if they contain some errors or are misused by others. Rather than wholesale rejection or uncritical embrace, the appropriate Lutheran posture to scientific theories is one of dialogue. One may rightly criticize some aspects or applications of a theory while affirming others. A theory which is false in its universal claims may still be helpful in a limited domain. A Christian scientist should not accept that materialistic evolution is the final and complete explanation of the origin and diversity of life, of consciousness, reason and morality, for that denies the essential role of God's creative Word. But that does not prevent the scientist from using the theory in more limited cases where it is empirically confirmed, such as studying resistance to antibiotics or treatments for HIV. Likewise, one can be skeptical of psychiatric approaches that rely almost exclusively on medication (because, for example, they ignore spiritual factors or alternative, cognitive therapies which accord the patient more dignity as someone made in the image of God), while granting the value of drugs in many cases.

It is precisely because Christians have a place to stand, on Christ, who is "the same yesterday and today and forever" (Heb. 13:8), that they do not have to lean on their own understanding (Prov. 3:5–6), including science, as a place for final answers. As Veith argues, this actually frees Christians to be both more skeptical and more open-minded toward the world's ideas than the secularist.[71] Having rejected a transcendent foundation, the secularist is more likely to invest a favorite theory with a kind of religious significance, sometimes precisely because it is thought to provide a substitute for God. Thus Richard Dawkins approves of Darwinian theory in part because he thinks it makes it possible to be "an intellectually fulfilled atheist."[72] Clearly this is to make a much stronger claim for the theory than the fallible empirical method and available data can support. This is no surprise, given the fact that humans are inherently religious, and as Luther explains, whatever we set our heart on and rely on for all good things is god for us.[73]

If we compare a scientific theory to a dance partner, the contrast is that the secularist may inappropriately cling to that partner as a place of final refuge,

---

[70] C. S. Lewis, *Perelandra* (New York: Scribner, 1944), 70. This phrase is also the title and leading theme of chapter 1 of Gilbert Meilaender's *The Taste for the Other: The Social and Ethical Thought of C. S. Lewis* (Grand Rapids: Eerdmans, 1978).

[71] Gene Edward Veith, *Loving God With All Your Mind: Thinking as a Christian in the Postmodern World* (Wheaton, IL: Crossway Books, 2003).

[72] Richard Dawkins, *The Blind Watchmaker* (New York: Norton, 1986), 6.

[73] Martin Luther, *The Large Catechism*, Part 1.2, *The Book of Concord*, ed. Robert Kolb and Timothy J. Wengert [Minneapolis: Fortress Press, 2000], 386 (hereafter KW).

while the Christian can and should hold the partner only lightly. The partner may be interesting and helpful, but it is not our spiritual spouse: that place is already taken by Christ. Or, to use a comparison to an automobile, Christian scientists should be happy to "test-drive" any scientific theory to evaluate its merits, but they should see as folly any attempt to preserve that theory in pristine form (by dismissing or rationalizing away the accumulation of contrary evidence) because it gratifies a displaced spiritual need.

6. A Christocentric approach to creation

A major problem with many well-meaning attempts to understand science in Christian terms is that they are implicitly deistic: God creates the universe and governs it through laws, but is otherwise uninvolved in it. This modern picture of a distant God and a spiritually empty nature is precisely what Lewis lamented in *The Discarded Image*. It is not enough to connect a "God of the philosophers" with nature. We should seek to recapture the idea of a God who is actively present in His continuing creation, preservation and providential shaping of this world. As we have seen, the fact that contemporary science may have little interest in this topic is no reason not to develop a complementary theology of nature. And it may be that, as it dialogues with scientific theories held lightly, there is mutual illumination that does not distort the proper message and purpose of Scripture or science. Paul tells us not merely that "all things were created" by Christ, but also that they were created "for him," and that "in him all things hold together" (Col. 1:16–17). This can be read as supplementing John's account that all things *were* created through the Word (John 1:1–3), by further affirming that Christ *is still personally present* as the unifying thread throughout the fabric of creation.

This authorizes what Harry Blamires calls the "sacramental cast,"[74] which sees everything created by God as testifying to Him and governed by His ongoing purposes. It provides a reason to resist the "nothing buttery" attitude of scientific reductionism. This attitude reflects the assumption that any apparently remarkable phenomenon is really *nothing but* something less remarkable: for example, morality is nothing but instinct, life is nothing but chemistry, and consciousness is merely a brain process.

In general the reductionist supposes that a created whole is nothing but the aggregate of its parts, and that we have a complete inventory and grasp of the parts. The Scriptures reject this view because we cannot fully understand what something is except in its relation to God. Thus God tells the prophet Jeremiah that He knew him before He formed him in the womb (Jer. 1:5), implying that what Jeremiah is as a person known by God cannot simply be reduced to the particular biological material formed during gestation.

---

[74] Harry Blamires, *The Christian Mind*, 173f.

Likewise, all the things God creates are what they are not finally because of what they are made of, but because of His intentions and purposes. Thus a scientific analysis of a human being into cells or particles will not reveal that he is made in the image of God or is personally known by God, but the latter remain part of the final truth about who and what that person is. In the same way, a socioeconomic analysis of parenthood or work will not disclose the truth that they are callings from God, and a psychological profile of a Christian friend will not reveal the fact that he is an instrument in God's hands to bring others to faith. And although modern science continues to speak of nature as governed by laws, which suggests a personal lawgiver, its methods cannot detect God providentially shaping all things to work together for good for those who love Him (Rom. 8:28).

Thus even where the reductionist paradigm works in science—and in many areas it is spectacularly successful—it should not be regarded as providing the whole truth. Relative to certain parameters (e. g., what is a thing is composed of or which of its properties can be measured quantitatively using the senses or physical instruments) it may give a satisfying explanation of phenomena. But the tractable, the measurable, and the quantifiable appearances of a thing do not exhaust it. In Kantian terms, *noumena* (things in themselves) are more than *phenomena* (things as they appear to us in experience), and the Bible may often reveal to us deeper qualities of things than science can discern.

As we have seen, it is dangerous and inappropriate to try to use science to "prove" scriptural truths, as if Scripture is nothing but a disguised textbook and as if science has final authority. But it is possible to point to scientific data which, combined with reasonable philosophical assumptions, provide good evidence for God's involvement in the natural world. The evidence itself consists of highly specific information found in nature, which cannot reasonably be explained by undirected, physical causes. Two examples of this are the fine-tuning of the laws of nature for complex, intelligent life and the detailed instructions for assembling living creatures found in DNA.

Fine-tuning

Since the 1970's cosmologists have discovered increasing evidence that the physical constants governing the four fundamental laws of nature (gravitation, electromagnetism, and the weak and strong nuclear forces) are not arbitrary, but are finely-tuned to permit a life-friendly universe. For example, as reported by Robin Collins, an expert in the philosophy of physics, "Calculations by Brandon Carter show that if gravity had been stronger or weaker by 1 part in 1040, then life-sustaining stars like the sun could not exist."[75] Astronomer Guillermo Gonzalez and philosopher Jay Richards also note

---

[75] Robin Collins, "The Fine-Tuning Design Argument: A Scientific Argument for the Existence of God," 2, available at: http://www.discovery.org/a/91.

how unlikely such stars are given the range of possible values for the forces of gravitation and electromagnetism: "mid-range stars are near the dividing line between convective and radiative energy transport ... a teetering balance between gravity and electromagnetism. If it were shifted one way or the other, main sequence stars would be either all blue or all red."[76] Similarly, a "change in the (strong) nuclear force strength (the force that binds particles in an atomic nucleus) by more than about half a percent ... would yield a universe with either too much carbon compared with oxygen or vice versa, and thus little if any chance for life."[77] If the force were significantly weaker or stronger, "no atoms could exist other than hydrogen,"[78] making life impossible.

These and many other extraordinary cases of fine-tuning have led sober-minded physicists to say some extraordinary things. For example, George Ellis, a British astrophysicist, said:

> Amazing fine tuning occurs in the laws that make this [complexity] possible. Realization of the complexity of what is accomplished makes it very difficult not to use the word 'miraculous' without taking a stand as to the ontological status of the word.[79]

Likewise, Arno Penzias, a Nobel-prize winning physicist, said:

> Astronomy leads us to a unique event, a universe which was created out of nothing, one with the very delicate balance needed to provide exactly the conditions required to permit life, and one which has an underlying (one might say 'supernatural') plan.[80]

Gonzalez and Richards extend this fairly standard fine-tuning argument by noting that our solar system, and particularly the Earth, are also locally fine-tuned to permit life. The Earth is shielded from comets by Jupiter and from the asteroid belt by Mars, and has an unusually large moon, which "stabilizes the rotation axis of its host planet, yielding a more stable, life-friendly climate. Our moon keeps Earth's axial tilt ... from varying over a large range."[81] This prevents climate fluctuations and temperature extremes that life cannot tolerate. In addition, the moon raises the ocean tides "creating the fecund intertidal zone" and is thought to contribute to ocean currents that

---

[76] Guillermo Gonzalez and Jay Richards, *The Privileged Planet* (Washington, DC: Regnery Books, 2004), 204.

[77] Ibid., 199.

[78] Robin Collins, "The Fine-Tuning Design Argument," 7.

[79] George Ellis, "The Anthropic Principle: Laws and Environments." *The Anthropic Principle*, F. Bertola and U.Curi, ed., (New York, Cambridge University Press, 1993), 30.

[80] Margenau, H and R.A. Varghese, ed., *Cosmos, Bios, and Theos.* (La Salle, IL, Open Court, 1992), 83.

[81] *The Privileged Planet*, 4.

"regulate the climate by circulating enormous amounts of heat."[82] According to Gonzalez and Richards, both a larger sun and a smaller one would be less favorable to life. Large suns have rapid changes in luminosity "more likely to lead to drastic climate changes" and generate asteroids; a small sun would brake the rotation of Earth giving it a cold, frozen side and an arid desert side, neither of which are life-friendly.[83] Finally, "the host planet ... needs to be about Earth's size to maintain plate tectonics, to keep some land above the oceans, and to retain an atmosphere."[84] From this it seems that the size, shape and relative location of the earth, sun and moon are fine-tuned for complex life.

Still more amazingly, it appears that the very same conditions that make the earth congenial to life also make it a good place for scientific investigation of the cosmos. The fact that the moon has the same visual size as the sun means that scientists on earth can observe "perfect" eclipses of the sun. In a "super-eclipse," the face of the sun (the photosphere) is covered by an object with a larger visual size. By contrast, a perfect eclipse is a total eclipse where the photosphere is covered by an object of exactly the same visual size and shape, making it possible to investigate the chromosphere and corona. "Of the more than sixty-four moons in our solar system, ours yields the best match to the sun as viewed from the planet's surface .... The sun is some four hundred times farther than the moon, but it is also four hundred times larger. As a result, both bodies appear the same size in our sky."[85]

Beyond that, it turns out that our universe is not a chaotic, confused mass of whirling debris in a state of flux, but is organized into discrete, stable clusters which can be studied independently of one another. As a result, scientists have been able to make progress in discovering simple laws, where newer laws build on the previous ones. Our universe exhibits "linearity and locality," meaning that we can reliably extrapolate from observing a small area to a law which holds throughout the universe.

> Linearity and locality are closely related to nature's long-term stability—another prerequisite for life and discovery. Our very ability to establish the laws of nature depends on their stability.[86]

This miracle, that the universe and the human mind are so ordered that scientists can discover beautiful laws was not lost on Einstein, despite the fact that he was neither an orthodox Jew nor a Christian. He wrote that

> *a priori* one should expect a chaotic world which cannot be grasped by the mind in any way ... [T]he kind of order created by Newton's theory of gravitation ... is wholly different. Even

---

[82] Ibid., 6.

[83] Ibid., 132–133.

[84] Ibid., 7.

[85] Ibid., 9.

[86] Ibid., 211.

if the axioms of the theory are proposed by man, the success of such a project presupposes a high degree of ordering of the objective world .... That is the "miracle" which is being constantly reinforced as our knowledge expands.[87]

So confident has modern science become that its best answers must be rational and beautiful, that even the atheist Nobel prizewinning physicist Steven Weinberg admits that scientists expect to find "beautiful answers" when they study fundamental problems, that the beauty in present theories points to the greater beauty of the final theory and indeed that a final theory would not be accepted "unless it were beautiful."[88]

Of course, none of this is proof, and it is always possible for a skeptic to suggest an alternative explanation. Some argue that fine-tuning is just an "anthropic coincidence," and we should not be surprised that the universe is calibrated to produce intelligent life like us, for only if this were the case would we be here to observe it. This argument misses the point, however, as John Leslie points out. [89] Suppose I am sentenced to execution by fifty sharpshooters, but to my surprise, they all miss. We would not consider it an adequate explanation of this surprising event to say, "Well, if they hadn't missed, you wouldn't be here to be surprised!" Yes, one must be conscious to be surprised, but that does not explain away the improbability of all those sharpshooters missing. We would look for some act of sabotage, an executive order, or a secret agreement among the sharpshooters (in other words, to intelligent design) to explain this highly improbable event. Likewise, the fact that we would not be here unless the universe were fine-tuned does not make it any less improbable that it is, and offers no explanation of why the fundamental forces of nature take the specific values that they do.

The realization of this fact has led other skeptics to propose the idea of a multiverse, according to which our universe is only one of a large (possibly infinite) number of universes. Given enough universes, almost anything might happen in one of them, and it is no longer so improbable that there is one supporting intelligent life. However, as different, causally isolated regions of space and time, these other universes are necessarily unobservable, and so the idea of a multiverse is untestable and speculative. And, arguably, it also violates Occam's razor[90] (which says that we should not multiply entities

---

[87] Albert Einstein, *Letters to Solovine* (New York: Philosophical Library, 1987), 131.

[88] Steven Weinberg, *Dreams of a Final Theory* (New York: Vintage Books, 1994), 165.

[89] John Leslie, "How to Draw Conclusions From a Fine-Tuned Cosmos," in Robert Russell, et al, eds., *Physics, Philosophy and Theology: A Common Quest for Understanding* (Vatican City State: Vatican Observatory Press, 1988), 304.

[90] This principle is named for William of Occam (1285–1349), though similar principles of simplicity, such as the idea that nature takes the simplest course, are found in the work of Aristotle, Ptolemy, and Aquinas. Occam's razor is the methodological principle according to which, other things being equal, scientists should prefer the simpler hypothesis. What this means is that we

beyond necessity), since a single, rational God is surely a simpler hypothesis that will explain the available data. In fact, as Robin Collins has pointed out, the idea of a multiverse does not even succeed in explaining away design, because it requires the mechanism of a "universe generator," and

> in all current worked-out proposals for what the "universe-generator" could be—such as the oscillating big bang and the vacuum fluctuation models ...—the "generator" itself is governed by a complex set of physical laws that allow it to produce the universes .... [I]f these laws were slightly different the generator probably would not be able to produce any universes that could sustain life.[91]

It is noteworthy that there is no hard evidence for the existence of such a universe-generator. It appears to be postulated not because any data require it, but because it would allow a naturalistic account of cosmology that excludes God. We should remember that resistance to God is not merely a matter of reason, but also a matter of will, a will which in natural man is turned in enmity away from God, and which seeks to efface all evidence of His involvement in the world. As Paul tells us, God has made His attributes plain within nature, but fallen man suppresses that truth (Romans 1:18–20).

Biological information

Origin of life researchers have concluded that life is far different in its complexity than Charles Darwin had thought.[92] In the 19th century, it was commonly supposed that living cells were undifferentiated blobs of protoplasm, and it did not seem so unlikely that these building blocks could have arisen spontaneously from inorganic chemicals. Since the discovery of DNA, however, it has become clear that every living cell contains elaborate instructions for the construction and regulation of proteins and protein machines. Just as the finely tuned constants of physics contain information that structures a life-friendly universe, so DNA contains information necessary to build and maintain living systems. In the natural world, a key difference between living and non-living systems is that the former exhibit specified complexity: not only are they highly complex, but that complexity is specified by the independent functional requirements of life. The British chemist and origin of life researcher Leslie Orgel explains:

> Living organisms are distinguished by their specified complexity. Crystals ... fail to qualify as living because they lack

---

should not "multiply entities beyond necessity," postulating more entities than are required to explain the phenomena.

[91] Collins, "The Fine-Tuning Design Argument," 10.

[92] For an excellent history of origin of life studies and a rigorous argument in favor of design, see Stephen C. Meyer, *Signature in the Cell: DNA and the Evidence for Intelligent Design* (New York: HarperCollins, 2009).

complexity; mixtures of random polymers fail to qualify because they lack specificity.[93]

The information in DNA is expressed in terms of four nucleotide bases, adenine, thymine, cytosine and guanine (abbreviated A, T, C, G), which represent a digital code analogous to the binary code of 0 and 1 used in a computer's machine language. Scientists discovered that these bases are not arranged in repeating sequences, but are highly "aperiodic" (non-repeating) like the sentences in a book. Further, when considering every possible sequence of these bases, it became clear that most would produce a non-functional result, which would not support a viable system.[94] Thus in living systems,

> The nucleotide base sequences in the coding regions of DNA are highly specific relative to the independent functional requirements of protein function, protein synthesis, and cellular life.[95]

It is generally agreed that there are just four possible types of explanation for this information: chance, necessity, a combination of chance and necessity, and design. Of these, chance has been roundly rejected because of the staggering complexity of even the simplest possible living organism:

> recent theoretical and experimental work on the so-called minimal complexity required to sustain the simplest possible living organism suggests a lower bound of some 250 to 400 genes and their corresponding proteins. The nucleotide sequence-space corresponding to such a system of proteins exceeds 4,300,000. The improbability corresponding to this measure of molecular complexity again vastly exceeds … the "probabilistic resources" of the entire universe.[96]

This is not surprising because in our experience chance has a very limited ability to produce coherent information: we might be fortunate enough to extract a short word out of the Scrabble bag, but even with a large number of tries we cannot reasonably expect to produce one of Shakespeare's sonnets.

---

[93] L. E. Orgel, *The Origins of Life on Earth* (New York: John Wiley, 1973), 189.

[94] Pursuing a Darwinian paradigm, many scientists expected the human genome to be full of non-coding "junk DNA," non-functional souvenirs of our evolutionary history. However, this assumption has been discredited by the discovery that the DNA is not "junk" but helps in such important processes as regulating genes and cell division. See "Identification and analysis of functional elements in 1% of the human genome by the ENCODE pilot project," *Nature*, 447 (14 June 2007), 799–816; "Exploring 'Junk DNA' in the Genome," *Science Daily*, June 16, 2007, <http://www.sciencedaily.com/releases/2007/06/070615091210.htm.>; Jonathan Wells, *The Myth of Junk DNA* (Seattle: Discovery Institute Press, 2011).

[95] Stephen C. Meyer, "DNA and the Origin of Life: Information, Specification, and Explanation," in eds. John Angus Campbell and Stephen C. Meyer, *Darwinism, Design, and Public Education* (East Lansing, MI: Michigan State University Press, 2003), 236.

[96] Ibid., 243.

Necessity (or "self-organization") claims that laws alone suffice to explain life, which would mean that some chemical law dictates the sequences of nucleotide bases. This also is highly implausible because laws are capable only of explaining repeating patterns (repeating events like thermal expansion, or repeating structures like crystals). However, in order for the sequences of nucleotide bases to serve as assembly instructions for functional, living systems, it is essential that they are not repetitive. If the nucleotide bases interacted by chemical necessity, "DNA would contain sequences awash in repetition or redundancy—much like the arrangement of atoms in crystals."[97]

What about the idea that chance and necessity could be combined to account for the information in living systems? What this really means is that natural selection can be applied before life appears (there are chance variations, some of which are favored by the law of natural selection), but natural selection can only operate on self-replicating, living systems—so this idea assumes the very thing it has to explain. As Theodosius Dobzhansky said, "prebiological natural selection is a contradiction in terms."[98]

Since these appear to exhaust the naturalistic resources for explaining life, it becomes reasonable to consider design. Yet the case for design is not simply negative (natural causes appear to be inadequate), which might seem like a "God of the gaps" argument from ignorance.[99] Rather, it is also a fact of our experience that various objects which exhibit specified complexity—such as computers, scientific theories, and novels—are regularly produced by intelligent agents and not by unintelligent causes. If intelligent agents have the known causal power to produce such artifacts, but unintelligent causes cannot do so, then if we see systems in nature that resemble these artifacts in their specified complexity, it is reasonable to infer an intelligent cause. Of course, it takes more argument (particularly philosophical argument) to make the case that this designer is God.

It is interesting that even some atheist intellectuals find the complex specified information in every living cell too much for undirected causes to explain. Antony Flew renounced his lifelong atheism in large part because "the findings of more than fifty years of DNA research have provided materials for a new and enormously powerful argument to design."[100] Likewise,

---

[97] Ibid., 253.

[98] Theodosius Dobzhansky, "Discussion of G. Schramm's Paper," in *The Origins of Prebiological Systems and of Their Molecular Matrices*, ed. S. W. Fox (New York: Academic Press, 1965), 310 "

[99] The "God of the gaps" argument as referenced here and elsewhere in the document refers to the logical fallacy that a "gap" in human understanding of some aspect of the natural world can be posited as "proof" for the existence and activity of God.

[100] Antony Flew and Gary Habermas, "My Pilgrimage from Atheism to Theism: An Exclusive Interview with Former British Atheist Professor Antony Flew," 5, available at: http://www. biola.edu/antonyflew/flew-interview.pdf.

atheist philosopher Thomas Nagel rejects the reductive materialism of neo-Darwinism in part because of the complexity of all life:

> [T]he coming into existence of the genetic code—an arbitrary mapping of nucleotide sequences into amino acids, together with mechanisms that can read the code and carry out its instructions—seems particularly resistant to being revealed as probable given physical law alone.[101]

On the other hand, Antony Flew only became a deist and, so far as we know, never embraced Christianity. And Nagel still holds out for the idea of "immanent teleology," according to which what drives the cosmos toward living, conscious, rational and moral beings are goal-directed processes fully within nature. This shows that, without the significant addition of philosophical principles, scientific "design arguments" have a limited ability to make the case for God. And even with those principles in place, a case for theism does not disclose who that God is. Without the clarity of revelation, therefore, the natural man is liable to shape the divine being in his own, idolatrous image.

Yet, by highlighting the role of information in structuring the cosmos and its inhabitants, design is richly suggestive of a God that governs the universe through His Word, and who is actively holding all things (cosmological and biological) together. While this science needs to be supplemented by a well-conceived theology of nature, it does provide materials congenial to a worthwhile, and sometimes mutually reinforcing, dialogue between faith and science.

7. Image of God theology and Christian anthropology

Reductive materialism attempted not only to replace a world charged with the grandeur of God with a purposeless machine, but also, and in a similar way, to redefine human beings. No longer are they conceived as embodied, rational souls made in the image of God. Rather, in the tradition of Julien Offray de la Mettrie (1709–1751), humans are thought to be no more than organic machines. Similarly, for Richard Dawkins, a living creature is simply "a survival machine for genes," and that includes us: "Next time you look in the mirror, just think: that is what you are too."[102]

Just as the impact of reductive materialism on the cosmos requires a fresh, Christocentric theology of creation, so its impact on human nature requires a similar theological response. Perhaps the most valuable resource here is careful articulation of image of God theology. The implications of this doctrine are sometimes neglected in Lutheran circles, because the Lutheran Confessions

---

[101] Nagel, *Mind and Cosmos*, 10.

[102] Richard Dawkins, *The Magic of Reality: How We Know What Is Really True* (New York: The Free Press, 2011), 74–75.

typically speak of the image of God in the narrow sense of *original righteousness*, which was lost in the Fall. This original righteousness was a gift that enabled our "knowledge of God, fear of God, and confidence in God."[103] But on account of the inherited sickness that is original sin, we "not only lack fear and trust in God, but also do not even have the power or gifts to produce fear and trust in God."[104] Since this has been lost, the image of God might seem irrelevant to understanding fallen human beings. However, as Nathan Jastram argues at length, Scripture also speaks of the image of God in a broader sense (humans are like God in various ways), and shows that in this sense, the image of God still remains.[105] For example, we learn that even after the fall, it is wrong to slaughter other humans like animals because the former are made in the image of God (Gen. 9:6).

What difference does it make to think that human beings are specially made in the image of God and still retain important remnants of that image? For one thing, it is clear that God provides us with special gifts so that we can serve as stewards of the rest of the world. This includes the intellectual and moral gifts required to practice science within God-pleasing boundaries, as we cannot steward nature effectively if we do not know how it works and what purpose it serves. If we unpack the various gifts presupposed by our stewardship obligations, we find an amazing range of competencies that go far beyond what is required merely to survive.

In order to carry out their obligations, stewards must persist as moral agents over time and be aware of that fact, so that they can plan and implement solutions to stewardship problems. While many animals are aware of items in their environment (such as food, predators, and mates), they do not seem able to conceive of themselves as persisting over time. This surely explains why they lack the sustained ability to transform the environment for the sake of long-term goals (farming, construction of permanent housing, transportation networks, etc.). It is also why none of these creatures appear to do anything like human science. Scientists must conceive of themselves as persisting over time. They can develop theoretical and technological solutions to problems, design experiments, and test their theories. These projects take time and presuppose that the investigator attempting to solve a problem is the same as the one who previously recognized the problem. They are also part of longer term projects, such as optimizing bandwidth for electronic communication, improving average fuel economy, eliminating malaria, or curing cancer.

Easy to overlook is that in order to be a steward of creation, one must have a concept of the natural world as distinct from oneself. While aware of

---

[103] "Apology of the Augsburg Confession," Article II (Original Sin), KW, 114.

[104] Ibid., 102.

[105] Nathan Jastram, "Man as Male and Female: Created in the Image of God." *Concordia Theological Quarterly* 68: 1 (January, 2004): 5–96.

specific objects in their immediate environment, the most intelligent animals still seem to have no concept of nature as a whole. It does not seem plausible that they have ever entertained the cosmological argument for God—in part because they have no concept of the cosmos as the totality of physical reality which they inhabit. Humans are dramatically different, and from before the time of Aristotle until the present, they have been very interested in cosmology. To be sure, the skeptical philosopher David Hume (1711–1776) poured scorn on the idea that humans could understand the cosmos:

> [E]ven if we do take the operations of one part of nature on another as our basis for judgment about the origin of the whole world (which is something we should never do), why would we select as our basis such a tiny, weak, limited cause as the reason and design of animals on this planet seems to be? This little agitation of the brain that we call 'thought'—what special privilege does it have that entitles it to serve as the model of the whole universe? [106]

However, Christian philosopher Blaise Pascal (1623–1662) anticipated and exposed a fallacy in Hume's critique of human capacities:

> Through space the universe grasps me and swallows me up like a speck; through thought I grasp it. [107]

Hume confuses *physical* limitations of the human thinker's body with *cognitive* limitations of the thinker's mind. The fact that our thought is correlated with a "little agitation of the brain" does not prevent us from thinking about the "whole universe." It might be noted that Hume himself has to assume we are capable of doing this in order to make his critique of theistic arguments, since he attempts to offer alternative explanations of the cosmos. This is why, of all creatures on earth, only human beings can consider why the universe came into existence, and ponder the significance of its apparent fine-tuning for intelligent life. Clearly God has provided humans with sufficiently powerful minds that we can think of the entire creation He entrusted to us.

In this sense we are like God—which is, unfortunately, also the root of our temptation to reach up and claim *to be* God. The godlike scope of human thought can tempt some people, including scientists, to believe that they can completely understand and control reality by themselves: the lure of Babel remains strong (Gen. 11:1–9). But Scripture reminds us that although in *some* ways our capacity for thought is godlike, we are not God, and our thoughts can never ascend to His heights.

[106] David Hume, *Dialogues Concerning Natural Religion*, http://www.earlymoderntexts.com/pdfs/hume1779.pdf (Copyright 2010–2015, Jonathan Bennett), Part 2, 13.

[107] Blaise Pascal, *Pensées*, trans. A. J. Krailsheimer (New York: Penguin Books, 1966), #113, 59.

For my thoughts are not your thoughts, neither are your ways
my ways, declares the Lord. For as the heavens are higher than
the earth, so are my ways higher than your ways. (Is. 55:8–9)

As Jastram has argued,[108] this means that though humans are like God,
they are called to a "middle road,"[109] with a proper balance of confidence
and humility.[110] On the one hand, as image-bearers called to steward the rest
of God's earthly creation, we can be confident that we are capable of doing
science well enough to care for the world and to serve our neighbor. But, on
the other hand, our intellectual gifts only enable us to grasp and control the
contingent, temporal order of nature. They do not help us to discern the ultimate reason why things are as they are.

Stewardship is a mandate to care for things *below* us, a mandate for
those specially made in the image of God to care for all the other living and
non-living creations *not* so made, and to preserve and develop that trust for
the sake of present and future generations. It is not a mandate to reach *above*
us and supplant God's role in providing guidance and salvation. Nor does it
authorize us to treat other people made in the image of God as if they were
merely part of the rest of creation which lacks that image. That is what is fundamentally wrong about seeing another human being merely as a collection
of cells or organs that might be harvested for some other purpose.

The image of God is also reflected in our ability to know the particular
kinds of creature we are called to husband. In the beginning, Adam was
allowed to name the creatures (Gen. 2:19), and it is arguable that these names
were not arbitrary but reflected natural kinds.[111] At any rate, scientists have
since developed detailed classificatory schemes for both the living and
non-living environment (e.g., taxonomies into phyla and species and the
periodic table of elements). For example, Carl Linnaeus (1707–1778), revered
as the father of modern biological taxonomy, was the son of a Lutheran pastor,
and his scientific work in botany and zoology was motivated by a profound
belief in the orderliness of God's creation. Scientists have also used observation and reason to discern regularities and laws that allow the effective
prediction and control of natural events, and the ability to synthesize useful
compounds and develop labor-saving technologies.

---

[108] Nathan Jastram, "Scientists Called to Be Like God," in ed. Angus Menuge, *Reading God's World: The Scientific Vocation* (St. Louis: Concordia Publishing House, 2004), 243–269.

[109] In this context, the phrase is due to Stanley Jaki, *The Road of Science and the Ways to God* (Chicago: University of Chicago Press, 1978), 87.

[110] Consider the case of a skilled surgeon whose abilities enable him or her to treat successfully medical crises that would have been impossible a generation ago. Yet, not every operation is a success.

[111] This was Luther's opinion. For discussion, see Harrison, *The Bible, Protestantism, and the Rise of Natural Science*, 249.

Among all God's earthly creatures, only human beings can know what nature is and what particular kinds of things are found there, so that these natural resources can be used to fulfill the so-called "cultural mandate" (Gen 1:28), which allows humans to develop nature into culture to serve their needs and purposes. However, we are not authorized to do this in just any way. Stewardship of nature is a trust, not an unrestricted gift. Our stewardship vocation is not a license to ravage and despoil nature. We do not own it: "The earth is the Lord's and the fullness thereof, the world and those who dwell therein" (Ps. 24:1); we are only caretakers, and together with our intellectual gifts, God also provides the moral capacities required to fulfill our obligation to be wise stewards. Here it is significant that the Noahic covenant God makes after the flood is made between God, human beings and "every living creature" (Gen. 9:8–11). Although these other creatures are not image-bearers and may be used for food (Gen. 9:1–3), still they were created good (Gen. 1:25) and therefore have intrinsic value, not merely instrumental value for our purposes. It is unwarranted to damage the non-human environment without need, not only because it harms future generations of people who depend on it, but because it shows disrespect for the value of a world God made good.

Here again, it is clear that humans are different from the most intelligent animals. Since these animals do not conceive of themselves as rational agents persisting over time, they cannot grasp moral rules that apply to their conduct over time.[112] Humans can understand such rules and hence have stewardship obligations that no other creature has. It really is up to us to use the world wisely for the sake of posterity.

As with a theology of nature, a developed theological anthropology can also find support in independent evidences. While Scripture's authority is inherent, it can aid the apologetic task to urge those who reject it to consider the scientific evidences and philosophical arguments which support our being made in the image of God. For example, neuroscientist Mario Beauregard and science journalist Denyse O'Leary have thoroughly exposed the poor science lying behind attempts to reduce the mind to the brain and to reduce religious experience to the product of malfunctioning "God spots" in the brain.[113] And eminent philosopher J. P. Moreland provides a rigorous defense of several characteristics of human beings that evidence their being specially made in the image of God, including the character of their consciousness, the nature of rationality, and their access to moral norms.[114]

---

[112] See Richard Taylor, *Ethics, Faith and Reason* (Englewood Cliffs, NJ: Prentice-Hall, 1985), 14.

[113] Mario Beauregard and Denyse O'Leary, *The Spiritual Brain: A Neuroscientist's Case for the Existence of the Soul* (New York: HarperCollins, 2007).

[114] J. P. Moreland, *The Recalcitrant Imago Dei* (London: SCM Press, 2009). Other excellent works in this area include Stewart Goetz and Charles Taliaferro, eds., *Naturalism* (Grand Rapids: Eerdmans, 2008) and Mark Baker and Stewart Goetz, eds., *The Soul Hypothesis* (New York: Con-

8. The theological underpinnings of modern science

We have seen that Christian theology provides a coherent rationale for doing science, conceived as a stewardship vocation, and that human beings are equipped to carry out that vocation as those made in the image of God. At a deeper level, Christian theology also provides the intellectual and moral foundation for supposing that science is a worthwhile project. It is easy to imagine that science simply developed as an extension of human curiosity and that it has little to do with background worldview. To the contrary, as many scholars have pointed out, most worldviews are *not* congenial to the idea that science is a feasible or valuable project.[115] As a matter of historical fact, it was Christian theology that provided the presuppositions that supported the rise of modern science.[116]

The feasibility of science

The idea that nature can be systematically investigated presupposes that it makes coherent sense, that there are some overarching rules or laws that explain its operation. Animism and pantheism discourage this idea because nature is viewed as a storehouse of local and capricious deities, so there is no reason to expect general principles or uniformities. By contrast, the Christian idea that nature is a book inscribed with a *logos* by a single author encouraged scientists to believe that there were rationally comprehensible, universal laws of nature. This understanding of the scientific task was explicit in the writings of some of the great founders of modern science. Thus Galileo wrote that science "is written in this grand book, the universe … in the language of mathematics."[117] Likewise, Johannes Kepler and Robert Boyle saw nature as a book inscribed with mathematical laws.[118] And, as the eminent historian of science John Hedley Brooke points out, these scientists assumed that the same *logos* at work in nature was also reflected in the reason of beings made in God's image.[119] This encouraged scientists to think that their minds were sufficiently attuned to the natural world that they could interpret and read

---

tinuum, 2011) and Stewart Goetz and Charles Taliaferro, *A Brief History of the Soul* (Malden, MA: Wiley-Blackwell, 2011).

[115] For an excellent comparative analysis of the impact of various worldviews, see Stanley Jaki, *The Savior of Science* (Grand Rapids: Eerdmans, 2000). He shows how a variety of philosophical and theological rivals to Christianity lead to stagnation and "still births" that obstruct scientific progress.

[116] See Nancy Pearcey and Charles Thaxton, *The Soul of Science: Christian Faith and Natural Philosophy* (Wheaton, IL: Crossway Books, 1994) and many of the essays in *Reading God's World*, ed. Angus Menuge.

[117] Galileo Galilei, "The Assayer," in *Discoveries and Opinions of Galileo*, trans. Stillman Drake (New York: Doubleday, 1957), 237f.

[118] Harrison, "Priests of the Most High God," 73–74.

[119] John Hedley Brooke, *Science and Religion: Some Historical Perspectives* (New York: Cambridge University Press, 1991), 19.

the text, discovering the laws of its operation. Without this idea that the rationality of nature and our minds reflect the same *logos*, with a common source in the mind of God, it might be as if nature were written in German, while humans could only think in French. As Pearcey concludes, "the doctrine of the creation (of the world and the human mind) provided the basic ontological and epistemological presuppositions for the scientific enterprise."[120]

More than that, important theological doctrines made a difference in the way the natural text was read. Following Aristotle, many scientists had supposed that science proceeds by discerning the essence of things, which will then tell us how they must operate. This encourages the idea that we can anticipate nature's course through metaphysical analysis rather than by observation and experiment. Without testing ideas against nature, many erroneous ideas were developed such as the idea that falling rocks "want" to reach their natural resting place. The decisive turn to the empirical method of modern science was inspired by the theological doctrine of *divine voluntarism*: as a free, transcendent agent, God governs the world as He chooses. Since God's thoughts and ways are above our own, and an infinite, perfect God may choose what finite, fallen beings would not expect, we are well-advised to go and see what the Lord has done. Since the natural text is the free creation of God, our goal should not be anticipation of its meaning (that risks *eisegesis*), but simply to discern what that text actually says (*exegesis*). As Peter Harrison argues at length, this approach was strongly encouraged by the Reformers' emphasis on the literal meaning of Scripture, a hermeneutic that was transferred over to the reading of the natural text.[121]

Kepler was also inspired in his search for cosmological laws by the idea that God provides for His creatures in reliable ways because He is a promise-keeper. Though God is free, He is not arbitrary and capricious. Out of love, He provides a stable and intelligible world. He can and does sometimes do miracles so that what usually happens turns out differently. Most of the time, however, He governs the world through predictable ordinances. Thus, in his astronomical work, Kepler "believed that he had discovered the part of God's providential plan that embodies the pattern of the cosmos, and the divine laws by which God regulated its moving parts."[122] To be sure, we now know that Kepler's "laws" are only approximations to the truth, and the history of science shows that even the most successful theories of the past are superseded and shown to be valid only in certain domains or under certain assumptions. This again illustrates the fact that good science involves a balance between legitimate confidence and proper humility. We are like God, but we are not transcendent over creation, and our will is not His will. So we must

---

[120] Pearcey, "How Science Became a Christian Vocation," 42.

[121] Harrison, *The Bible, Protestantism, and the Rise of Natural Science.*

[122] Peter Barker and Bernard Goldstein, "Theological Foundations of Kepler's Astronomy," *Osiris* 16 (2001), 113.

49

buckle down and use our gifts to discover *something* of how God governs this world, realizing that it is most likely only part of the truth. For in science as in all things, our lot in this life is to "know in part," as "in a mirror dimly" (1 Cor. 13:12), due to our finite, fallen limitations.

The value of science

Science is not only feasible: it is worth doing. As we have seen, science naturally flows from the cultural mandate to shape nature into culture. But there are also more specific reasons Christians with the appropriate gifts can and should do science. Science is inherently worthwhile because God created the world good: the world is full of things worth knowing about. Science is also a way of glorifying God, by showing His marvelous handiwork. It provides a storehouse of evidence for God's existence that can be marshaled by natural theologians and Christian apologists.

But above all, science is a vehicle of thought through which human beings are enabled to love and serve their neighbor. First, through science, we have developed all manner of products which improve our quality of life. It is hard to imagine (or to want to imagine) a world without vacuum cleaners, refrigerators, furnaces, air conditioners, washing machines, telephones, televisions, and computers.

Second, science helps us to do something to mitigate the consequences of the Fall. We cannot heal the universal, hereditary infection of sin. But we can use scientific discoveries to ameliorate human suffering. Whole classes of disease can sometimes be eradicated from the world, and even when they cannot, science allows dramatic improvements in the quality and quantity of earthly life for the sick. We cannot extinguish the corrupt desire to treat other human beings as tools and possessions, which explains the rise of the "new slavery" even as we celebrate the abolition of older forms.[123] But we can drastically improve the living and working conditions of many people through improved housing, clean water and labor-saving technology. And even when it is the misuse of science which leads to problems (such as many of our environmental problems, like toxic waste), still, science will likely play an important part in any effective response.

Christianity provides powerful moral motivations for doing science because it sees that in all things, Christians are called to love others as God first loved them (1 John 4:7–12). This love is not merely words or a feeling, but is found in concrete actions of service. We love one another in and through our vocations, including the scientific vocation. Indeed, as Veith reminds us, it is really God at work in us, loving and serving our neighbor.[124] The scientist,

---

[123] See Kevin Bales, *Disposable People: New Slavery in the Global Economy*, rev. ed. (Berkeley, CA: University of California Press, 2012).

[124] Gene Edward Veith, *God at Work*.

like other workers, is God's instrument, providing services that help to preserve the world and meet our neighbor's temporal needs.

Yet science is not everything, and the Christian scientist is only one member of the body of Christ which includes many other members with different but critically important functions. It may be the scientist who develops a new strain of wheat. But when that scientist drives to the store to buy a loaf of bread made using that wheat, he still relies on farmers, truck drivers, bakers, and store clerks (not to mention automotive and road construction workers). Even if scientists are, in some respects, "smarter" than other people, and can claim to be the "eyes" of a modern, technological society, while these other workers are merely its hands, still (drawing on St. Paul's vivid analogy for the church as a "body"): "The eye cannot say to the hand, 'I have no need of you'" (1 Cor. 12:21). Reflection on our creaturely interdependence in God's economy is a good antidote to the inflated veneration some give to scientists. Without the scientist, the farmer might have a poorer yield. But without the farmer, the scientist would most likely starve. So the Christian scientist should see his or her work realistically, as an important, God-pleasing opportunity to contribute to a diverse, interdependent community of many other workers. All Christians together, regardless of our various vocations, are called to "grow up in every way into him who is the head, into Christ, from whom the whole body, joined and held together by every joint with which it is equipped, when each part is working properly, makes the body grow so that it builds itself up in love" (Eph. 4:15–16).

Chapter II
Historical Context

1. Introduction

Despite the tremendous resources which theology affords scientific inquiry, we see today a stunning disconnect between faith and science. At best, faith provides encouragement to do scientific work honestly and well, which is a good thing, but it has nothing to say about the deeper meaning of that work. This is due to two major and closely related movements of secularization. During the Enlightenment, reason was transformed from a servant of the faith to an autonomous judge of objective reality, and nature was transformed from a divine work of providence to an autonomous world machine. How did we lose the sense that nature is *God's world* and that reason is *God's gift* to understand it? That is the focus of this chapter. The aim is to give a brief, historical account that explains how we arrived at the default perception of the relation between science and faith predominant today.

The story begins with the revolt against Aristotle (384–322 BC), and in particular his appeal to final causes. Aristotelian metaphysics recognized four causes: the material cause (what is something made of?), the formal cause (what is its structure, shape or form?), the efficient cause (what produced the effect or made it come into being?) and the final cause (for what purpose was it brought into being?). A simple illustration is given by the chef's preparation of a dinner. The material cause of the dinner is all of the ingredients. The formal cause is the recipe for combining those ingredients which accounts for the form of the final product. The efficient cause is the cook himself, as without him the dinner would never come into existence. And the final cause (the goal or purpose of all this) is to provide the dish requested by the guest. As modern science arose, the idea that science could discern the final cause (the goal or purpose) of natural events was increasingly viewed with skepticism. For example, did science really have to speculate on the goal or purpose of burning wood in order to understand how wood burns?

Many of those who criticized the appeal to final causes in science (like Galileo, Bacon, and Descartes), continued to believe that nature was God's other book, but over time, that critique inspired others to outright attack on the natural theology which claimed to read that book's messages (section 2). Increasingly, thinkers of the Enlightenment encouraged a diminished reverence for revelation and believed that our own faculties were sufficient for understanding nature. This led to the rise of autonomous, universal reason (section 3). Combining this view of reason with the rejection of natural theology, nature itself came to seem a self-sufficient, Newtonian world-machine (section 4). At first this was usually combined with a belief in a remote deity who started the whole system in motion (deism), but as time went on, God seemed redundant even in that capacity. It appeared to many that the only thing necessary to understand any natural phenomenon was some other natural phenomenon that caused it. This fueled *naturalism,* according to which either nature is all there is—*philosophical naturalism*—or, if there is something more, like God, still He is irrelevant to understanding the natural world—*methodological naturalism* (section 5). With this foundation in place, it no longer seemed appropriate to speak of scientists as "priests in the book of nature." Increasingly, science was not viewed as a vocation. Instead, it was seen as a *profession* in the contemporary, secular sense: a scientist is a functionary in the modern, industrial state (section 6). So the severing of nature from God's providential care and of reason from divine illumination yielded science as a non-vocation. This has done damage not only to faithful scientists, who experience *angst* because they do not see how to relate their faith to their work in meaningful ways, but also to the general public, who suffer from a disconnect between what is most valuable to them, and what they can claim to be fact. It is one of the many reasons that the default belief system of many religious people in countries like America today is what leading sociologist of religion Christian Smith dubs "moralistic therapeutic deism"[125]: God has been evacuated from nature and almost all of life, hanging on only as a therapeutic life coach if times get bad (section 7).

2. The attack on final causes and the decline of natural theology

In surveying his philosophical predecessors, Aristotle discerned a gap in the type of causes they discussed.[126] Many fixated on material and efficient causes. For example Thales (625–545 BC) suggested that everything was made of water while Empedocles (490–430 BC) suggested Earth, Air, Fire and Water for material causes and Love and Strife for efficient causes. A few thinkers realized that one must also account for the shape or structure of the outcome (formal causes). Thus Pythagoras (570–495 BC) suggested that nature is governed by an underlying mathematical harmony (an idea which, much later, the Lutheran astronomer Johannes Kepler [1571–1630] saw as deeply congruent with the Christian idea of a world governed by a rational Lawgiver). But none of them, thought Aristotle, had considered the most important causes of all, those that provided the purpose or goal of things (final causes). The idea of final causes dominated subsequent thought during the scholastic period, and even many thinkers of the modern period, such as

---

[125] Smith and Denton, *Soul Searching.*

[126] See Antony Kenny, *A New History of Ancient Philosophy, Volume 1: Ancient Philosophy* (New York: Oxford University Press, 2007), chapters 2 and 6.

William Paley (1743–1805), saw its value for natural theology.[127] However, natural theologians were concerned that Aristotle's own scheme, which located final causes within nature, was not compatible with God's sovereign rule over creation. For example, as early as the 13th century, Etienne Tempier, the Bishop of Paris, expressed his recognition that the Aristotelian account of Forms, as natures within substances that dictated their final purpose, would abridge God's freedom to govern creation as He saw fit.

> In 1277 Etienne Tempier...issued a condemnation of several theses derived from Aristotelianism.... The condemnation of 1277 helped inspire a form a theology known as voluntarism, which admits no limitations on God's power. It regarded natural law not as Forms inherent *within* nature but as divine commands imposed from *outside* nature.[128]

At the same time, some natural theologians supposed, not without reason, that the created world was designed to support those made in God's image, and so they attempted to read off God's final causes for things from their evident benefits to humanity.

No doubt this led some natural theologians to forget that God made all things good—so that all of nature has an intrinsic value regardless of whether it serves human interests. But it was very helpful in some areas of science, including medicine. For example, Walter Charleton's (1619–1707) study of the uses of blood, respiration, and muscles assumed that these structures existed for a purpose: "Walter Charleton, sometime physician to Charles I, spoke of 'the Uses of the Blood,' 'The *Final Cause*, or *Use of Respiration*,' 'the *Use of the Muscles.*'" [129] Likewise, William Harvey's (1578–1657) investigation of the heart assumed that it had a discernible function. End-directed thinking was vitally important not only in anatomical studies like Charleton's and Harvey's but also in the history of botany and zoology, as shown by the pioneering work in taxonomy by John Ray (1627–1705), and Carl Linnaeus (1707–1778). The work of these scientists was strongly guided by their natural theological beliefs in an ordered, purposive creation. As Peter Harrison concludes, "The search for divine purposes in the natural order provided a clear religious warrant for a pursuit that might otherwise have been regarded as the accumulation of vain and futile knowledge."[130] Today, and despite the fact that final causes are typically rejected by science, they are still a useful

---

[127] Paley's most famous work is *Natural Theology or Evidences of the Existence and Attributes of the Deity*, published in 1802.

[128] Nancy Pearcey and Charles Thaxton, *The Soul of Science: Christian Faith and Natural Philosophy* (Wheaton, IL: Crossway Books, 1994), 31.

[129] Harrison, *The Bible, Protestantism, and the Rise of Natural Science*, 170, italics in the original.

[130] Ibid., 184.

construct for understanding complex, biological systems. As even the contemporary naturalistic philosopher of biology Michael Ruse concedes:

> We treat organisms...as if they were manufactured, as if they were designed, and then try to work out their functions. End-directed thinking—teleological thinking—is appropriate in biology because, and only because, organisms seem as if they were manufactured, as if they had been created by an intelligence and put to work.[131]

On the other hand, some natural theology over-reached by claiming to read God's intentions directly from a beneficial consequence that might be a coincidence. For example, Noël-Antoine Pluche (1688–1761) went so far as to claim that

> the woodworm, which eats the hull of ships, actually contributes to harmonious international relations, for it provides opportunities for some countries to sell to others pitch with which to protect ships' hulls: 'Thus does this little Animal, which we so much complain of as being troublesome and injurious to us, become the very Cement which unites these distant nations in one common Interest.'[132]

This is a nice story, but is there any way to test it? And has God Himself revealed to us that this is the real reason for the woodworm? The answer to both questions is negative. It is at this point that appeal to final causes invites fanciful speculations that cannot be checked against hard evidence. More cautious natural theologians, similar to today's proponents of Intelligent Design, realize that one should carefully distinguish between inferring design and inferring intention. An archaeologist may discover an item which is obviously designed—an artifact of some sort—without immediately knowing *why* it was made. For example, an item in the shape of a blade might be a utensil, a tool for working leather or wood, a weapon, or a ceremonial item with no ordinary use. Likewise, with the invention of the microscope, many saw evidence of a world brimming with design long before they had any knowledge of what microorganisms do.

> [T]he microscope was able to show that even the most modest of creatures had been designed with a remarkable precision... and the world of minute creatures came to exercise a unique fascination over seventeenth-century minds.[133]

---

[131] Michael Ruse, *Darwin and Design* (Cambridge, MA: Harvard University Press, 2004), 268.

[132] Harrison, *The Bible, Protestantism, and the Rise of Natural Science*, 175. The embedded quote is from Noël Pluche himself, *Spectacle de la Nature: or Nature Display'd*, 5th revised and corrected edition, volume III (London: 1770), 318.

[133] Ibid., 172–173.

It was only later that the pioneering work of Ignaz Semmelweis (1818–1865) and Louis Pasteur (1822–1895) established that some microorganisms are responsible for disease, and saw the need for disinfectant and the sterilization of medical instruments. And it was not until the twentieth century that the incredible complexity within each living cell was uncovered.

> The entire cell can be viewed as a factory that contains an elaborate network of interlocking assembly lines, each of which is composed of a set of large protein machines. Why do we call the large protein assemblies...machines? Precisely because, like the machines invented by humans...these protein assemblies contain highly coordinated moving parts.[134]

The tendency of some natural theologians to claim too much—to peer further into providence than fallen man is capable of—led some to be skeptical of the whole approach. And there was a concern that if all of nature reflected God's design, this would make God complicit in the natural evils of predation, parasitism and disease.[135] As Cornelius Hunter has argued, Darwin and others who were skeptical of natural theology objected to design (or final causes) at least in part for theological rather than scientific reasons, because of a conviction that God would not be intimately involved in conforming such an imperfect world to His purposes.[136] Apparently, there was insufficient attention paid to how the Fall complicates our understanding of design in the world: we are not seeing the world as God originally intended it to be, since creation itself is distorted, subject to the Fall's effects (Rom. 8:20–21). Our own faculties are also prone to error in judging how God "ought" to have done something.[137] While some proponents of natural theology undoubtedly claimed too much, Hunter argues that the theological assumption that God is not actively at work in His world may have led scientists to the opposite extreme: have they developed a naturalistic "blind spot" that makes it impossible to infer design no matter what the evidence.[138]

Even before Darwin, it seemed to many of the early modern philosophers and scientists that appeal to final causes was liable to anthropomorphic

---

[134] Bruce Alberts, "The Cell as a Collection of Protein Machines: Preparing the Next Generation of Molecular Biologists," *Cell*, vol. 92 (1998), 291.

[135] For example, Charles Darwin wrote to Asa Gray on the 22nd of May, 1860: "I cannot persuade myself that a beneficent & omnipotent God would have designedly created the Ichneumonidæ with the express intention of their feeding within the living bodies of caterpillars, or that a cat should play with mice." Available at: http://www.darwinproject.ac.uk/letter/entry-2814.

[136] Cornelius Hunter, *Darwin's God: Evolution and the Problem of Evil* (Ada, MI: Brazos Press, 2002).

[137] Since death came through the Fall, nature before the Fall would have been quite different than it is presently.

[138] Cornelius Hunter, *Science's Blind Spot: The Unseen Religion of Scientific Naturalism* (Ada, MI: Brazos Press, 2007).

speculation and was in any case unnecessary for empirical science. Thus, quite early in the scientific revolution, Francis Bacon (1561–1626) argued that humans have a tendency to project their own agency onto the world, supposing that a being like themselves is the ultimate explanation of anything mysterious:

> As it strives to go further, [the human mind] falls back on things that are more familiar, namely final causes, which are plainly derived from the nature of man rather than of the universe....[139]

Thomas Hobbes (1588–1679) made much the same point in critiquing the use of final causes in dynamics:

> [M]en measure, not only other men, but all other things, by themselves; and because they find themselves subject after motion to pain, and lassitude, think everything else grows weary of motion and seeks repose of its own accord.[140]

It was not only materialist philosophers like Hobbes, but also Christian scientists, such as Galileo (1564–1642) and Robert Boyle (1627–1691), who worried that it was inadvisable to read final causes into nature. Their concern, like Etienne Tempier's, was that if final causes were understood as implanted within nature, this would threaten God's sovereignty. For if these causes operate independently of God, then apparently not even He can alter their effects. By contrast, if God is free to direct nature as He sees fit, and these final causes remain under the governance of His will, then science must adopt a humble, empirical method, content to discover what God has chosen to do in the natural world.

Thus, Galileo (1564–1642) believed that the only way to discover the Law of Descent governing the rate of acceleration of objects in free-fall was by empirical testing.[141] One had to look and see how God had chosen to govern the world, rather than speculate *a priori* on the supposed essential natures of the falling objects. Boyle argued that matter is in itself completely passive, unable to give an ultimate account of its motion, and that it was also affected by non-mechanical "active principles," which he thought were involved in some chemical reactions and life processes. In this way, God was the final cause of all motion in the world and was also immanently involved in it, via these active principles.[142]

For Boyle, in both the case of matter and active principles, God works through means. Standard physical science (e.g., typical physics and

---

[139] Francis Bacon, *The New Organon*, Bk. I, XLVIII.

[140] Hobbes, *Leviathan* I.2 in Works, ed. William Molesworth (Aalen: Scientia, 1962) III, 3 f.

[141] For details, see chapter 6 of Rom Harré's *Great Scientific Experiments: Twenty Experiments that Changed our View of the World* (Mineola, NY: Dover Publications, 2002).

[142] See Pearcey and Thaxton, *The Soul of Science*, 87–88 and Angus Menuge, "Interpreters of the Book of Nature," in Menuge, ed., *Reading God's World*.

chemistry) is focused on these means (secondary causes) and so has no need to appeal to primary final causes. But since biology is interested in the origin of life, it pushes us beyond secondary causes. This explains why Boyle thought final causes had no value in understanding ordinary physical causation, and yet at the same time was an enthusiastic supporter of the argument for divine design in biology.[143] He realized that passive matter does not itself explain its complex, functional organization in the organs and body plans of living beings. For this, only the primary, final causation of God would suffice. The ultimate reason that such organization exists is that God designed it for a purpose.

Although it had a number of rationales, a tragic consequence of the well-intended exclusion of final causes from science, quite often advanced by Christians and on theological grounds, was a weakening of the understanding of God's providence. If we cannot talk about what natural events are for in science, how do we visualize God as actively shaping those events to His ends? It is technically compatible with such a scientific account that the eyes of faith can discern a providential pattern, but if people look to science for objective knowledge of the world, and science finds final causes to be redundant, some may conclude that God's providential care of the world is an illusion. This already seems a very different vision of science than Kepler's. As we saw in the previous chapter, Kepler did not make a rigid distinction between science and natural theology, seeing the laws of nature as God's "providential plans." Although the causal connection between particular pairs of events need not disclose any divine purpose, Kepler thought that the existence of general laws governing the cosmos in reliable ways was a clear sign of that purpose.

A second problem is that the anti-anthropomorphic arguments against final causes go too far. Christians understand that we are made like God (in His image), and that although His thoughts and ways are above our own (Is. 55:8–9), we can learn about God by what He is like. Our clearest source is the revelation of God in the man Jesus Christ. To the charge that all talk of God's purposes is anthropomorphic, we may reply that God made us *theomorphic* (in His likeness), and also that in Christ, God Himself is anthropomorphic (He made Himself like one of us), thus creating a built-in affinity between human beings and God. Informed by this faith, and mindful of the limitations of finitude and sin, we should affirm that we can know something of what God has done in nature, and may indeed see signs of His providential hand. Although we may sometimes read into natural events motives that are not there, that does not make us incapable of ever discerning God's work in the world.

---

[143] See Edward B. Davis, "Science as Christian Vocation: The Case of Robert Boyle," in *Reading God's World*, ed. Angus Menuge, 206–207.

It is a great irony of history that philosophers and scientists who were for the most part practicing Christians set in motion a train of thought whose unintended consequence was a diminution of the sense of God's providential care of the world and of our special status as beings made in the image of God. By fixating on the gift and not its Giver, even devout Christians have repeatedly found ways to increase their distance from God.[144]

3. The rise of autonomous reason

Another example of the same trend is the exaltation of human reason as a faculty capable of discerning objective truth independent of divine revelation.[145] Two of the most audacious philosophical works of the early modern period are Francis Bacon's *The New Organon*, and Rene Descartes' *Meditations*. In both works, there is a rejection of tradition and external authorities as a basis for knowledge in favor of the use of our unaided faculties, such as reason and experience.

In *The New Organon*, Francis Bacon (1561–1626) is merciless (and often unfair) in his critique of the Aristotelian paradigm for science that had dominated the scholastic period. He says that "the sciences we now have are no more than elegant arrangements of things previously discovered, not methods of discovery or pointers to new results."[146] In other words, scholastic science was stagnant and unfruitful because it deferred to the authority of the past instead of devising better methods for discovering new knowledge. He charges that the scholastics were guilty of attempting to "anticipate" nature on the basis of preconceived metaphysics and erroneous methods of scientific reasoning, when they should have been content merely to "interpret" nature through a patient accumulation of data.[147] Bacon is audacious enough to claim that what we need is to construct a whole new method of scientific inquiry. Just as whole new worlds were found by use of the lodestone, Bacon thought that a reformed inductive method would accelerate the pace of scientific discovery. His approach had two major components. First, the investigator must purge his mind of preconceived bias—the idols of the mind[148]—so that he does not try to anticipate what nature must do, but is open to discovering the truth about natural phenomena. Then he must collect large and varied

---

[144] Consider also St. Paul's warning in Romans 1:18–25 about the perennial human tendency to focus on the gift and not the Giver, to worship created things rather than the Creator.

[145] On the wages of Enlightenment rationalism, see also the CTCR report, *The Natural Knowledge of God: In Christian Confession and Christian Witness* (St. Louis: The Lutheran Church—Missouri Synod, 2013), 21–24.

[146] Francis Bacon, *The New Organon*, ed. Lisa Jardine and Michael Silverthorne (New York: Cambridge University Press, 2000), 34 (Book I, aphorism VIII).

[147] Bacon, *The New Organon*, 38–39 (Book I, aphorisms XXVI–XXX).

[148] Ibid., 40–56 (Book I, aphorisms XXXIX–LXVII).

samples of facts, so that his conclusion is an interpretation of the phenomena driven by those facts and tested against them.[149]

On one hand, there is something admirable about Bacon's insistence that we should interpret nature rather than anticipate its course. This fits well with the ideas that nature is a book which God freely inscribed with His messages, and that we are called to read and interpret them. On the other hand, by disconnecting this rational method from the revealed truth about ourselves, Bacon is surely tempted to exaggerate our ability to purge our minds of bias. We cannot remove the original sin that infects all of our faculties, and which constantly biases our reason to accept falsehoods that it wants to believe in and attempt to rewrite reality after our own preferences.

Like Bacon, René Descartes (1596–1650) was unashamed in his disdain for his intellectual predecessors.

> Medieval philosophers had seen themselves as principally engaged in transmitting a corpus of knowledge … Renaissance philosophers had seen themselves as rediscovering and republicizing the lost wisdom of ancient times. It was Descartes who was the first philosopher since Antiquity to offer himself as a total innovator; as the person who had the privilege of setting out the truth about man and his universe for the very first time. Where Descartes trod, others followed: Locke, Hume, and Kant each offered their philosophies as new creations, constructed for the first time on sound scientific principles.[150]

Descartes boldly proposed that, independent of past authorities, our own reason can provide an antidote to our vulnerability to error. In the *Meditations*, Descartes observes that our senses and dreams can deceive us into thinking there are realities which are not there.[151] But even if there were a supremely powerful demon that deceives us as much as possible, still we must exist as thinking things in order to be deceived. Descartes goes on to argue for the existence of a perfect God who would not allow people to be systematically deceived about the natural world. This does not mean that we cannot make mistakes: errors occur, Descartes explains, because we do not restrain our will to affirm or deny only those things which we understand.[152] However, a perfect God would not so make us that we are mistaken in our involuntary,

---

[149] This is the main topic of the second book of *The New Organon*. Bacon shows how his method of "true induction" applies to scientific investigation of the nature of heat by gathering various tables of data in which heat is present, absent, or present in varying degrees.

[150] Anthony Kenny, *A New History of Western Philosophy, Volume 3: Modern Philosophy* (New York: Oxford University Press, 2006), 40.

[151] René Descartes, "The Meditations," in *The Philosophical Writings of Descartes*, Volume II, trans. John Cottingham, Robert Stoothoff and Dugald Murdoch (New York: Cambridge University Press, 1984).

[152] René Descartes, "The Meditations," Meditation IV.

innate beliefs about the nature of reality—such as our belief in the external physical world and in other minds.

On the one hand, Descartes' reasoning did make room for God, whom Descartes viewed as the creator and continuing sustainer of the world.[153] Yet, on the other hand, his method assumes that reason can disclose the structure of reality without the illumination of revelation or the regeneration of faith. In the *Meditations*, Descartes' main contribution to the foundations of science was the idea that the essence of matter was extension in space. This led him to think that the idea of a vacuum (empty space) was self-contradictory and that all motion was by direct contact (mechanical causes) in a plenum packed with matter. Unaided reason led Descartes to conclusions scientists now regard as false (e.g., they acknowledge that vacuums exist and that neither gravitation nor electromagnetism require a mechanical medium). Descartes' limited reason was unable to disclose many marvelous things about the natural world undreamed of in his philosophy.

But much more disturbing than the specific errors of specific modern thinkers is the general tendency to suppose that reason can "go it alone." Like Prometheus stealing fire from the gods, modern man has attempted to sever one of God's greatest gifts, human reason, from its root in the divine reason. The result is a lack of humility, an overreaching pride that supposes humans can solve their various problems by themselves. What this neglects is that all reasoning requires assumptions, and that its conclusions are only as good as those assumptions permit. If our foundation is what seems indubitable to fallen, finite reason, we are ignoring the clear light from above that discloses reality from a vantage point unconditioned by finitude and sin. It is only by starting with God's revelation about the nature of creation, including ourselves and the nature of our sin, that we can hope to discern reality as it is.

As Jastram argues, we can learn an important lesson about the proper role of human reason in science by reflecting on the Greek myth of Daedalus and Icarus.[154] Daedalus builds artificial wings of feathers, wax and string, and urges his son Icarus to fly with him, cautioning him to find a path midway *between* heaven and earth.[155] But Icarus ignores the warning and flies too close to the sun: the wax melts, the wings disintegrate, and Icarus plunges to his death. The point of the story is not that humans should scorn their reason and turn away from science. If this were right, then humans would never have learned to build aircraft and space shuttles. Rather, Daedalus' advice to Icarus was to find a *middle way* for reason, one that allows investigation of

---

[153] See the masterful analysis of Daniel Garber, *Descartes' Metaphysical Physics* (Chicago: The University of Chicago Press, 1992).

[154] Nathan Jastram, "Scientists Called to be Like God," in Menuge, ed., *Reading God's World*, 243–269, 264–266.

[155] See the portion of Ovid's retelling of the Greek myth in his *Metamorphoses*, quoted in Nathan Jastram, "Scientists Called to be Like God," 265.

new possibilities but does not, like the people of Babel (Gen. 11), attempt to achieve godlike knowledge that is beyond our creaturely limitations. In other words, our reason is sufficiently *above* nature that we can hope to understand it well enough to be its stewards, but it is sufficiently *below* God that it cannot achieve the absolute certainty of an omniscient God. As the great Jesuit historian and theologian of science Stanley Jaki argued, this middle road gives just the right balance of confidence and humility to support sound scientific investigation.[156] It is neither so timid that science seems beyond our ability, nor so proud that it promotes *hubris*, claiming that science provides the ultimate answers that are God's alone.

4. The Newtonian world machine

Descartes hoped that his mechanical natural world still left God in charge as the primary cause of motion.[157] Likewise, Isaac Newton (1643–1727) believed that his physics captured the motions of the planets but did not explain their wise arrangement in a stable solar system. He said in the *General Scholium*: "This most elegant system of the sun, planets, and comets could not have arisen without the design and dominion of an intelligent and powerful Being."[158] As we will see, a great irony of history is that Newton, who was devoutly religious, developed his physics in such a way as to refute materialism and *make room* for God, yet what was later called "the Newtonian world machine" appeared to be a closed, autonomous, materialistic system in which even God could not intervene.[159]

Like Robert Boyle, Newton believed in both mechanical causes (which require the contact of particles) and active principles which could operate without any such medium.[160] Newton rejected the Cartesian paradigm according to which all causation is by contact because it supported the materialism of Thomas Hobbes and seemed to lead inevitably to atheism. He boldly proposed that the force of gravitation was an active power which could act across empty space with no mechanical medium. He was careful to say that gravity in no way excluded God's governance of the universe: on the contrary, gravity was itself a means by which God controlled the phenomena.[161]

---

[156] Stanley Jaki, *The Road of Science and the Ways to God*, cited in Jastram, "Scientists Called to Be Like God," 267.

[157] This case is well made by Daniel Garber in chapter 9 of his *Descartes' Metaphysical Physics*. While some of Descartes' ideas may have encouraged deism, Garber shows that Descartes himself was far from deism, believing that it was only because of God's continuing, sustaining influence that the cosmos remained in existence moment by moment.

[158] "General Scholium," in eds. Timothy McGrew, Marc Alspector-Kelly and Fritz Allhoff, *Philosophy of Science: an Historical Anthology* (Malden, MA: Wiley-Blackwell, 2009), 177.

[159] See Pearcey and Thaxton, *The Soul of Science*, chapter 4.

[160] Ibid., 89–90.

[161] Ibid., 90.

When he said *hypotheses non fingo* (I feign no hypotheses), he intended that gravity was simply a postulate that could be used to account for the relative motions of bodies and was not an ultimate explanation for the motions observed. In other words, gravity was proposed as a means by which God controlled those motions. Indeed, Newton also expressed an early version of the fine-tuning argument, because he realized that the masses and velocities of the heavenly bodies in the solar system were finely tuned to support a stable system.[162] While his universal laws of motion explained many things, they did not explain the specific value of the gravitational constant, and he was aware that a significant increase or decrease in that constant would cause the solar system either to collapse or to fly apart.

As the Enlightenment progressed, the ideas of active principles and the providential control of God were increasingly rejected. It did not help that Newton made the mistaken suggestion that God's periodic intervention would be necessary to maintain the stability of the solar system because of perturbations in planetary orbits. This view led him to be ridiculed by other scientists and philosophers, who thought that Almighty God would not design a cosmos that requires constant adjustments and tinkering.[163] Pierre-Simone Laplace (1749–1827) showed that these perturbations were in fact quite regular and did not lead to long-term instability or require intervention. This demonstration was later regarded as iconic of the ability of physical systems to maintain themselves, and to reject appeals to special divine providence as a "God of the gaps" fallacy, that argues erroneously from our ignorance of a natural cause to the conclusion that there must be a supernatural cause. At the same time, active principles were reinterpreted as fundamental powers of matter itself, so that matter did not need a special intermediary for God to govern it:

> Matter came to be regarded as self-sufficient, and Newton's active powers were absorbed in the materialistic philosophy he had hoped to refute. The irony is that this materialistic, mechanistic philosophy then came to be called the "Newtonian" worldview.[164]

This brash attempt to reduce the natural world to matter in motion came at a huge cost. Since the only properties of matter which could be studied by natural science were impersonal ones—like the extension, location, figure and motion of particles, the so-called "primary qualities"—the entire inner mental life of people was excluded from scientific reality. The colors, sounds, tastes, smells, and textures a person experiences were relegated to the subjective realm of "secondary qualities" that arise when our senses interact with

---

[162] Ibid., 91.

[163] Ibid.

[164] Ibid., 92.

the primary qualities of matter, but matter itself does not have the secondary qualities. In other words, most of what human beings call "life"—the way we experience things—is not the way things really are. Instead, we live in a virtual reality of subjectivity that creates a barrier between us and the natural world conceived as a world-machine devoid of subjectivity.[165]

At the same time, a self-sufficient world does not seem to need God's presence and on-going guidance. In the 18th century, the French Encyclopedists—like Jean-Baptiste d'Alembert (1717–1783), Denis Diderot (1713–1784), and Baron Paul-Henri d'Holbach (1723–1789)—used the Newtonian worldview to attack the "superstitions" of the past. By this they meant revealed religion, arguing that autonomous reason had triumphed in disclosing an autonomous nature. Some of the thinkers of this time, like François-Marie Voltaire (1694–1778), embraced deism, believing that God could be known from reason and nature alone. Voltaire held that God had created the world as a vast clockwork system that ran on by itself and did not require, or allow, further intervention. Others, like d'Holbach, embraced full-fledged materialism and atheism. As a result, reason was used to dismiss miracles as impossible, pre-scientific ideas, and religious texts that included miraculous accounts were subjected to historical criticism and assumed to contain legendary material.

Despite their low view of revelation, at least those Enlightenment thinkers who were deists thought they had some good arguments for God's existence. They thought that a mechanical world that does not need God's constant intervention gave greater testimony to His wise craftsmanship. Many people followed Descartes in holding that human beings clearly transcend the physical world because they had souls. The subjectivity that physical science could not find in the material world showed that we are something more than a material being. So it seemed for a while that we had good evidence in ourselves that there was something more than the Newtonian world machine. This could allow us to reconcile ideas like free will and our moral responsibility to God's laws with an otherwise impersonal universe that was deterministic and amoral.

5. The rise of Naturalism

Deism, however, proved to be an unstable halfway house as naturalistic thinking expanded its domain.[166] In his *Dialogues Concerning Natural Religion*, David Hume (1711–1776) cast doubt on any attempt to argue from the character of the natural world to the nature of deity. For example, if we argue

---

[165] For a well-known critique of this view, see C. S. Lewis, *The Abolition of Man* (New York: Macmillan, 1947).

[166] On the rise of Enlightenment naturalism, see also the CTCR report, *The Natural Knowledge of God: In Christian Confession and Christian Witness*, 21–24.

from the good in the world to the existence of a good God, why can we not argue from the evil in the world to the existence of an evil God?[167] Following the earlier lead of Thomas Hobbes (1588–1679), Julien Offray de La Mettrie (1709–1751), a physician, asked why the same mechanistic approach applied to the natural world around us could not be applied to human beings. His studies led him to the view that man himself is a machine—a machine in a world of machines.[168] And Baron d'Holbach (1723–1789) concluded that if we are subject to the same kind of causation we see in the physical world, we must not have free will.[169]

This corrosive skepticism did not immediately lead most thinkers to embrace a naturalistic worldview. This is largely because, despite the ideological crusade of the Encyclopedists—who are in many ways the intellectual forebears of today's New Atheists (Richard Dawkins, Daniel Dennett, Sam Harris and the late Christopher Hitchens)[170]—there were many defenders of natural theology and, in particular, biological design, well into the nineteenth century. After the classic work *Natural Theology* (1802) of William Paley (1743–1805), there were many other great works of natural theology, such as the contributions of William Whewell (1794–1866) and Charles Babbage (1791–1871) to the *Bridgewater Treatises*. These are the works of men of scientific and philosophical genius who were not intimidated by David Hume or the French Encyclopedists. In fact, in his treatment of the argument from design in *The Dialogues Concerning Natural Religion*, Hume himself had admitted that alternatives to divine design, such as the self-organization of matter due to unknown powers, were far less plausible. Hume even anticipates the modern design argument by apparently conceding that a library of self-reproducing books (uncannily similar to a contemporary understanding of DNA) would surely point to a designing intelligence.

Naturalism, therefore, could not hope to gain a strong foothold until the argument from design was unseated. Two major factors came to the aid of a naturalistic worldview. The first was the scientific theory of natural selection proposed in Charles Darwin's *On the Origin of Species* (1859). After studying the selective breeding of livestock, the range of species found in the Galapagos, and a variety of fossils and geology, Darwin concluded that the apparent design of living creatures was really the result of natural causes. In any given population of creatures, there would always be variation (whose source Darwin did not know) and some creatures would happen to be equipped with

---

[167] David Hume, *Dialogues Concerning Natural Religion and Other Writings* (New York: Cambridge University Press, 2007).

[168] Julien Offray de la Mettrie, *Machine Man and Other Writings* (New York: Cambridge University Press, 1996).

[169] See Baron Paul Henri d'Holbach, *The System of Nature* (Manchester, UK: Clinamen Press, 1999), chapter XI.

[170] Vox Day makes this connection very clear in his *The Irrational Atheist* (Dallas: Benbella Books, 2008).

features that gave them an adaptive advantage, increasing their chances of survival and reproduction. If the source of these features was heritable, then over time and assuming no great change in the environment, creatures with those features would tend to predominate in the population. So chance variation and natural selection could produce creatures that looked as if they had been especially designed to be well-adapted to their environments.

Darwin did not merely propose a "new" scientific theory (in fact, the idea was not that new, being anticipated by the work of Denis Diderot and Darwin's grandfather Erasmus). More important, Darwin proposed a whole new *method* for science which removed the need to talk of design, something which Boyle and Newton had made room for, at least in the background. While Kepler, Boyle and Newton had recognized three modes of causation—chance, necessity and design—the Darwinian methodology recognized only two. Many later scientists and philosophers took this as a mandate for methodological naturalism. According to methodological naturalism, while scientists can believe in intelligent causes, a truly scientific explanation can only appeal to the undirected, unintelligent causes of chance, necessity, and their combination. If this is so, then a complete scientific account of reality can be given without ever appealing to the intelligent causation of a designing God.

As Michael Ruse points out, however, Darwin's theory was not at first widely accepted and he failed to found "a professionally based area of biological science."[171] This was mainly because Darwin had no mechanism to explain the variation of creatures, and because many scientists maintained that there were fixed boundaries between species. While natural selection might explain variation within a species, it could not account for transitions between two species. The proposed mechanism came only later in the "Darwinian synthesis" with Mendelian genetics in the 1930's. With the subsequent discovery of DNA, and the suggestion that the main source of variation was mutation and other undirected changes to the instructions in DNA, the modern neo-Darwinian paradigm emerged.

But this entrenchment of a naturalistic theory of the variation of life was not the only factor that led to the ascendance of naturalism. The other was a parallel, philosophical development that encouraged an increasing number of thinkers to believe in scientism, the view that the naturalistic style of science as currently practiced was the only reliable source of knowledge about the world. The beginnings of this scientism can be seen in the work of the encyclopedists, who dismissed tradition and revelation in favor of what unaided, scientific reason could discern. The view was given a further push by the philosopher Immanuel Kant (1724–1804). In his magnum opus, *The Critique of Pure Reason*, Kant argued that our concepts are only valid of the world of experience (*phenomena*) and cannot tell us how the world really is in

---

[171] *Darwinism and its Discontents* (New York: Cambridge University Press, 2006), 24.

itself (we cannot access the *noumena* or things in themselves). From this, Kant concluded that metaphysical speculation about God, souls, and the moral law could not claim to be *knowledge*, even though he argued that all of them are presupposed by practical reason when we think about morality. After Kant, it seemed to many that science provides knowledge of the empirical world, but we cannot have *knowledge* in matters of religion or ethics, the beginnings of the "fact/value" divide.

Scientism was given further support by the work of Auguste Comte (1798–1857), who proposed the philosophy of positivism, according to which theology and metaphysics were outmoded, and empirical science was the only rational means of governing human society. Similar views were held by the Vienna Circle, a group of scientists and philosophers who met at the University of Vienna in the 1920s and early 1930s, including Rudolf Carnap (1891-1970), Victor Kraft (1880–1975), and Moritz Schlick (1882–1936). These thinkers advocated an austere empiricist epistemology that came to be known as logical positivism, according to which traditional metaphysics, religion and morality were non-cognitive (they could not be known or reasonably believed), because their statements were not amenable to empirical scientific investigation.

Logical positivism was popularized by Alfred J. Ayer (1910–1989) in his highly influential work, *Language, Truth and Logic* (1936). According to Ayer's "verification principle," a statement is literally meaningful only if is either true by definition (like '2 + 2 = 4' or 'A bachelor is an unmarried man') or verifiable in principle by some empirical observation or test. The consequence was that the statements of metaphysics, religion and ethics, being neither true by definition nor empirically testable, were declared to be literally meaningless. This did not imply that the statements of these disciplines had no meaning at all. For example, Ayer suggested that since the statements of ethics are typically expressed with a great deal of passion, perhaps they are merely disguised, indirect reports of our emotion. According to this view, known as emotivism, "Murder is wrong" is an expression of a strong feeling of disapproval for murder, while "Kindness is right" expresses a strong feeling of approval for kindness.

If naturalistic science is content to say that it reveals what can be known about reality under the limitation of naturalistic assumptions, then, of course, it is consistent with the existence and operation of supernatural forces which exceed its ability to explain. But if naturalistic science is combined with scientism, then the conclusion may be drawn that if science cannot detect the supernatural, then the supernatural does not exist. By similar arguments, not only miracles but souls, objective moral values, and God Himself are declared to be unknowable.

In the academic philosophical world, logical positivism has been roundly rejected because it is self-refuting and is inadequate even to make sense of science. Logical positivism is self-refuting because, as a philosophical theory, it cannot claim to be true by definition and because it is not verifiable by observation. Therefore, by its own lights, logical positivism is literally meaningless and at best an expression of emotion. And despite its pretensions to exalt science as the only way of knowing, logical positivism is actually incompatible with scientific practice, since scientists frequently postulate unobservable particles and forces to explain what they can observe, and also rely on unobservable entities like numbers and logical relations to formulate their theories.

But the cultural residue of scientism is still with us in the widespread assumption that there is no such thing as metaphysical, religious or moral *knowledge*. At the practical level of everyday life, this is the legacy of naturalism, which makes people unable to see how what is believed in faith could be known to be true. It is one reason apologists find it so hard to convince contemporary people that there is hard evidence for the resurrection as a historical *fact*. For many, the resurrection has already been placed in a noncognitive realm, since the assumption is that there could not be evidence for a supernatural event. Science is by definition naturalistic and if something cannot be known scientifically, it cannot be known at all. As a result, the resurrection and other miraculous claims of Christianity are relegated to a subjective realm accessible only by faith.

6. Science as a profession

Parallel with the rise of the idea that nature is an autonomous machine governed by purely undirected causes, there was a move away from the idea that science is a vocation, a way to be a priest in the book of nature, to the modern idea that science is a profession governed by standards independent of revelation. It is a revealing fact that this move was in part engineered by scientific materialists, like Thomas Huxley (1825–1895), who sought to position modern science as a rival and successor to the Christian church as a locus of cultural authority. While students of nature were called "natural philosophers" and "natural theologians" from the time of the scientific revolution until the nineteenth century, the coining of the new term "scientist" by William Whewell (1794–1866) in 1834,[172] signaled the appearance of a new and independent profession. Clergy who had played a large role in previous scientific work were supplanted by a newer, more secularized breed of investigators more targeted on serving the needs of the modern, industrialized state.

> [W]hereas previously in many of the scientific disciplines—and in natural history in particular—clergymen had played a predominant role, this was to change dramatically over the course

---

[172] Peter Harrison, "'Priests of the Most High God, with Respect to the Book of Nature': The Vocational Identity of the Early Modern Naturalist," in Menuge, ed., *Reading God's World*, 61.

of the [nineteenth] century.... The deliberate attempt on the part of some of the newly designated "scientists" to replace the clergy at the pinnacle of the professions was accompanied by a rhetoric that suggested the sciences were a kind of surrogate religion. "Darwin's bulldog," Thomas Huxley (1825–1895), thus wrote that he and his scientific brethren were members of a "church scientific."[173]

While only a minority of today's scientists share such hostility toward religion, this fact about how science achieved its high status as a modern profession by distancing itself from the church goes some way to explain why today's scientists do not see a clear connection between the official standards and those governing their faith. The deep connection between theology and science, which had been expressed and developed by so many previous scientists, was no longer seen as appropriate to a discipline that could claim its own authority independent of divine revelation.

7. The roots of moralistic therapeutic deism

In a recent landmark work, Christian Smith and Melinda Denton reported the findings of a major survey of the religiosity of American teens, "the largest, most comprehensive and detailed study of American teenage religion and spirituality conducted to date."[174] What they found confirms that the divorce of science from theology and an unquestioned assumption of scientism has sadly disfigured the faith of many young people today. Regardless of whether they belong to religious communities that are officially Christian, Jewish, or Muslim, the survey showed that the default belief system of a majority of American youth is *moralistic therapeutic deism*. The wages of naturalism have exiled God from ongoing, providential care of His world (*deism*). God is "not particularly involved in one's affairs—especially affairs in which one would prefer not to have God involved."[175] Strict deism is revised however, because people still want the comfort of religion (the *therapeutic*): "Deism ... is revised ... by the therapeutic qualifier, making the distant God selectively available for taking care of needs... like a combination Divine Butler and Cosmic Therapist."[176] What lies behind the therapeutic dimension of this emasculated faith is the assumption that God is not really knowable (since He is unscientific), but He is there to make us feel better subjectively.

> This is not a religion of repentance from sin ... of building character through suffering ... of basking in God's love and grace....
> It is about attaining subjective well-being, being able to resolve

---

[173] Harrison, "Priests of the Most High God," 79

[174] *Soul Searching*, 7.

[175] Ibid., 164.

[176] Ibid., 165.

problems, and getting along amiably with other people.... [One person surveyed said:] 'When I became a Christian ... it always made me feel better.'[177]

Likewise the *moralistic* dimension is subordinated to the therapeutic modifier. The idea that there is an objective moral law of God is dismissed as unknowable, reflecting the presupposition of scientism. Instead, what moralism means here is: "being the kind of person that other people will like, fulfilling one's personal potential, and not being socially disruptive .... [One teen said:] 'It's just whatever makes you feel good about you'."[178]

What this shows is that the wages of naturalism have not merely made it easier for people like Richard Dawkins to be intellectually fulfilled atheists. They have also led many religious people to radically revise their understanding of the Christian faith. The faith no longer consists of revealed truth claims about who God is, how He wants us to live, and what He has done to save us from our inability to live up to his expectations. Instead, faith is reinterpreted as little more than choosing to have a relentlessly positive attitude about life in the terms of a cosmic Bobby McFerrin's, "Don't worry, be happy," or a Pharrell Williams's "happiness is the truth." Such "happiness" is grounded not in Christ's forgiveness, but in the belief that we have no original sin and need no Savior.

We can expect that even many Christians who are scientists will be influenced by moralistic therapeutic deism. And so, instead of seeing science as a God-pleasing vocation—a way to serve God by using His intellectual gifts to study His other book—science is viewed as an autonomous profession, while religion provides a sense of comfort for those questions of meaning and value that science cannot address. This is the two-story mind described by Nancy Pearcey.[179] The lower story of objective fact is governed by naturalistic science. In the upper story of values, religion and morality live on, but only as subjective, private phenomena.

The great idea of vocation, that shows how scientific work has objective meaning and worth and which connects God's plans and providential care of the world with human work, is absent. This is why it is so vital to help Christians who are scientists recover that understanding of providence working in and through both the natural world and the vocation of the scientist. In this way, Christian scientists will rightly see themselves as unified wholes as they go about their work, and not radically divided beings consisting of two disconnected halves.

---

[177] Ibid., 163–164.

[178] Ibid., 163.

[179] Nancy Pearcey, *Total Truth: Liberating Christianity From Its Cultural Captivity* (Wheaton, IL: Crossway Books, 2004).

8. Conclusion

This chapter has sketched the major historical sources of the problematic conception of the relationship between faith and science in the contemporary world. The revolt against final causes led to an increasingly mechanistic picture of the world, and this made it harder to visualize how God maintained His providential care of all creatures. Reason transitioned from humble servant of the faith to an autonomous magistrate able to judge the contents of objective reality. The world itself came to seem like an autonomous machine, making deism seem the best option for believers in God. Skepticism about natural theology and the soul led some to embrace outright materialism. For about a century brilliant defenses of natural theology kept materialism at bay, but then Darwin undermined the argument from design and the logical positivists positioned naturalistic science as the only way to know reality. Science no longer seemed like a vocation but appeared to be an independent profession with its own authority.

The fall-out of these historical developments is that contemporary people have a hard time seeing any deep connection between faith and science, as Christianity is no longer viewed as a source of objective truth. Faith is viewed by definition as non-cognitive, an attitude of mind that does not embrace any definite knowledge. This is one of the main sources of the moralistic therapeutic deism prevalent in our youth. Today, Christian theologians and philosophers are swimming upstream when they argue that science is an objectively meaningful vocation, and that the Christian faith makes claims that we can know to be true.

Chapter III
Philosophical Issues

1. Introduction

Philosophy can help thoughtful Christians to identify the worldview assumptions that influence their perception of whether science can be pursued as a legitimate calling from God. In this chapter, we will begin with some of the ideas that have proven problematic for Christian scientists, since they either exclude or compromise important claims of faith. The goal here is to show that these ideas derive from extra-scientific ideologies that the Christian can and should reject. Then we will seek to show that, in fact, Christian theology provides many assumptions that are highly congenial to good science, and argue that there is no reason to divorce faith from the work of a Christian scientist.

2. Philosophical problems for the scientific vocation

As we saw in the last chapter, a consequence of the Enlightenment was that human reason was increasingly seen as an autonomous judge of all things. Behind this perception, two negative assumptions were at work. The first assumption was a denial of the full reality of sin: either original sin was rejected altogether or it was assumed that reason was not seriously infected. In both views, the idea of "total depravity," that all of our faculties have been distorted and misdirected as a result of sin, is not taken seriously. The second assumption was a denial of the status of Scripture as the inspired, infallible, inerrant word of God.[180]

The second assumption was manifested in several critical responses to Scripture, some more skeptical than others, but all of them united in denying that Scripture is the supreme authority over human judgments. The most skeptical claimed that Scripture was no more than a human attempt to understand the divine—a denial of inspiration, that reduces Scripture to an ordinary human work like Homer's *Odyssey*. Others, slightly less skeptical, claimed that while Scripture is indeed a response to the divine, and so perhaps inspired, the resulting text thoroughly reflects the intellectual and moral limitations of its authors. In this view, the Holy Spirit is unable to or chooses not to overcome. In this view, divine inspiration interacts with human fallibility to produce a mixture of God's truth and human error, and reason must be

---

[180] For a more detailed account of the infallibility and inerrancy of Scripture, see chapter 4.

used to differentiate the good and bad parts of Scripture. A popular version of this view is that Scripture is reliable in its theological and "spiritual" claims (especially in its claims about how human beings may be saved), but not in its "secular" claims concerning matters of historical or scientific fact.[181]

The combination of these two assumptions leads to the idea that reason is the best instrument for distinguishing truth and error in Scripture. And in science, it led to the view that a scriptural faith provides no guidance for the scientist. Reason thus becomes the only judge both of God's Word and of God's world.

Further, these assumptions lead to two troubling consequences for the Christian scientist. First, it can easily seem that science is liable to prove Scripture wrong, which may either dissuade a Christian from going into science for fear of what they may find, or lead them to compromise the faith because they think that science has shown at least some of its claims to be simply untenable. Secondly, Christian scientists may find it impossible to see how their faith could possibly provide insight about how their professional work should be done.

To be sure, Scripture does not claim to supply the techniques (or means) of science (such as how to devise experiments or to test theories), but it does not follow that it has nothing important to say about the nature and purpose of science. To allow autonomous reason to make these latter determinations may encourage Christian scientists to pursue their work in ways that make coherent sense and yet are not God-pleasing because they violate His moral boundaries for their vocation.

Over time, autonomous reason also encouraged the development of a number of ideologies which are either hostile toward, or in significant tension with, the Christian faith. Both historically and psychologically, the rise of the idea that reason can manage to discover truth by itself is closely tied to the idea that the physical world can manage by itself, in the sense that the world is a closed system of law-governed matter. As we saw in the last chapter, this materialistic view became increasingly prevalent during the Enlightenment, and many claimed that human beings are no more than physical machines passively obedient to physical laws.

Contemporary Christian scientists, who wish to pursue their vocation faithfully in light of Christian truth, are strongly advised to study materialism. They should learn how to recognize its implications and critique its assumptions, as this ideology has had an enormous impact on the main-

---

[181] This is the typical view of neo-orthodox theology, which seeks to protect the Gospel from historical investigation by insisting that it belongs to a special realm of supra-history accessible only by faith. In this view, it does not matter if the Scripture contains erroneous historical claims as they have no impact on the Gospel. This view seems flatly inconsistent with Paul's insistence that if Christ was not raised, our faith is futile (1 Cor. 15:17). We will show the inadequacy of this view as a model for biblical exegesis in the next chapter.

stream, institutionalized conception of what science is and does. While materialism is the central dogma, radiating out from it are a variety of subsidiary views which reflect its influence in one way or another. So we will first discuss materialism and then consider these further ramifications. Our goal is to clarify what the basic claims are, why they are in tension with the Christian faith, and how they can be resisted by a thoughtful Christian scientist.

a. Materialism

A worldview is an ostensibly coherent account of the world which includes foundational assumptions of metaphysics (what is real?), epistemology (how do we know?) and ethics (how should we live?). As developed in the modern period, materialism is a worldview which makes two main metaphysical claims.[182] First, it says that the bedrock of reality is purely physical: at the foundation of all things, we find only the sort of objects and forces disclosed by physical science, such as elementary particles and electromagnetism. Second, it says that anything else that exists is dependent on this physical bedrock. Perhaps minds and moral values exist, but if they do they reduce to, or at least wholly depend on ("supervene" on, "emerge" from), the physical—and so have no independent reality.

In contemporary philosophy, there are three main kinds of materialists, distinguished by how they treat phenomena that appear to transcend materialistic categories, such as consciousness, free will, the soul, and moral values. Eliminative materialists simply assert that such phenomena do not really exist: they are an illusion that will not be recognized in our "final theory" of reality.[183] Reductive materialists claim that the apparently transcendent phenomena are actually identical to physical objects or states like brains or brain states.[184] Non-reductive materialists admit that these phenomena are something more than the physical bedrock, but say that the phenomena nonetheless supervene on or emerge from that bedrock.[185]

In any of these views, the physical defines the boundaries of what exists: there cannot be any entities which are independent of the physical. Thus (unless they radically redefine the concepts in ways that obviously differ from

---

[182] For a recent, systematic exposition and critique of materialism, see George Bealer and Robert Koons, eds., *The Waning of Materialism* (New York: Oxford University Press, 2010). For a more accessible (but profound) critique of the central planks of materialism, see Thomas Nagel, *Mind and Cosmos*.

[183] See for example, Paul and Patricia Churchland, *On the Contrary: Critical Essays: 1987–1997* (Cambridge, MA: MIT Bradford Books, 1999). For a more accessible account, see Patricia Churchland, *Touching a Nerve: The Self as Brain* (New York: W. W. Norton and Company, 2013).

[184] A prominent example is philosopher Jaegwon Kim. See, for example, his *Mind in a Physical World: An Essay on the Mind-Body Problem and Mental Causation* (Cambridge, MA: Bradford Books, 2000).

[185] Probably the most famous proponent of this view is philosopher John Searle. See, for example, his *Freedom and Neurobiology: Reflections on Free Will, Language, and Political Power* (New York: Columbia University Press, 2008).

traditional theistic beliefs[186]), materialists typically deny the existence of God and the human soul, and they also often deny objective moral values.

In the Christian view, God is a pure spiritual (immaterial) being who is not composed of, or dependent on, physical particles or forces: God existed as a wholly non-physical being before the physical universe even existed. Likewise the soul is traditionally understood as an immaterial element which, while designed to be integrated with a human body in a single whole person, transcends the body, so that at physical death and before the resurrection, the soul can exist without that body.[187] Moreover, the objective moral values recognized by Christian theism are not derived solely from nature but ultimately from the will of a transcendent, supernatural being.

A clear recognition of the direct incompatibility between Christian theism and materialism is essential here because the influence of materialistic ideas on contemporary science will often be unconscious. Most fundamentally, it is easy to assume that science as currently practiced is able to disclose the full truth about reality and not to notice that much of science aims only to detect materialistic entities. Thus if such science by its very nature is not looking for (or able to detect) God, the soul or objective moral values, all this should tell us is that science (at least so practiced) is a limited instrument, not that these transcendent entities do not exist. If science is not even looking for X (or is unable to detect X if it is looking for it), the failure of science to find X tells us literally nothing about the existence of X.

More specifically, consider each of the three kinds of being denied by materialism: God, the soul, and objective moral values. All scientific observations and measurements depend on physical organs (such as eyes and ears) and instruments (microscopes, telescopes, spectrophotometers, seismographs, etc.). These organs and instruments are (at least normally) directly sensitive only to physical entities and processes. So if one focuses on the immediate causes of an observation or a measurement, these will typically be physical variables. But nothing follows from this about the existence or

---

[186] Thus a process theologian or a pantheist may speak of "God," but this is a reference to some immanent feature of nature (or to nature as a whole), and not to a being that transcends nature as in Christian theism. Likewise, some "Christian physicalists" may speak of the soul, but for them the soul is simply the form or organization of physical matter, which is not what traditional Christian theists mean by the soul. Likewise, for consistent materialists, "moral values" typically refer to properties determined by the capacity to feel pleasure and pain (as in Peter Singer's utilitarianism) or to the result of "reflective equilibrium" as we discuss our moral intuitions (as in Sharon Street's moral anti-realism), but this is not at all the idea of a transcendent moral law binding human behavior.

[187] It is important to note that in the beginning God designed us as integrated wholes of mind, body and spirit (1 Thess. 5:23), and that the separation of the soul from the body and our need to be raised from the dead are consequences of human sin (Rom. 6:23). Thus the Christian affirmation that God can maintain our souls in existence at physical death is a reflection of God's mercy despite our tragic disobedience. It is not, as in gnosticism, a picture of our ideal existence. The body is not, as the gnostics taught, a prison-house of the soul: God intends to reintegrate soul and body at the resurrection.

non-existence of a non-physical being like God. Indeed it may be that when we take a broader view of things, the best explanation of the human ability to discern the natural kinds of creatures that populate nature and the laws that govern their physical behavior is that God made these creatures and laws, and also made our minds in such a way that we are attuned to their discovery. It is important for the Christian scientist, therefore, to distinguish clearly between primary and secondary causes. Most of the time, scientists are engaged in exploring the immediate causes within nature (secondary causes) of an interesting phenomenon. They are not looking for the ultimate explanation of why such phenomena exist, why such phenomena are correlated with those immediate or secondary causes, or why such phenomena are even intelligible to the human mind (primary causes). With some justification scientists can often (if not always[188]) say that questions of primary causation are the province of philosophy and theology. But the important point is this: to the extent that science looks only for secondary causes of phenomena, it is simply silent on the matter of primary causes, and so has nothing directly to say about the existence (or non-existence) of God.

This is important because a number of atheist scientists have tried to claim that science somehow *disproves* (or counts against) the existence of God.[189] For their argument to get started, these atheists would first need to show that the science in question was looking for God and capable of detecting His presence. Otherwise, a simple response is to say that is not surprising that scientists who were not looking for God and/or were not able to detect Him found no evidence of His existence. If we investigate a windowless room, we can find no evidence for the existence of the Sun. This is true, but we also cannot discover any evidence against the existence of the Sun. This is because our mode of investigation was incapable of discovering the Sun even if it did exist. So it is worth asking such apologists for atheism exactly why they think their theories and observations have any bearing on the issue of God's existence. Unless they can show that their investigations concern the existence of primary causes, they are simply irrelevant to the question of God's existence.

Some similar points apply to the soul. Neurological observations and measurements can reveal the state of the brain, as our senses and instruments (such as various brain scanning techniques) are responsive to physical variables. But the fact that these observations and instruments are not capable of directly detecting the soul is not by itself a reason to think that the soul does not exist. To be sure, there may be broader facts about human cognition that

---

[188] It is arguable that some areas of science make a consideration of primary causes unavoidable, for example, when science theorizes about the origin of the universe, or the fact that it appears to be fine-tuned for both intelligent life and scientific discovery.

[189] See for example, Richard Dawkins, *The God Delusion*; Victor Stenger, *God: The Failed Hypothesis. How Science Shows That God Does Not Exist* (Amherst, NY: Prometheus Books, 2008); Lawrence Krauss, *A Universe From Nothing*.

are best explained by postulating a soul.[190] Most of the time, however, scientists are not attempting such a grand explanation, but are merely focusing on the local and proximal causes of observed events which, unsurprisingly, are typically physical.[191] So again, the findings of such limited inquiries are typically irrelevant to the existence of the soul. When scientists (more usually, materialist philosophers) claim that science has somehow disproved the existence of the soul, we should ask whether their methods of investigation were capable of detecting the soul's presence or absence in the first place.

In the case of objective moral values, a great deal of confusion has been caused by a systematic ambiguity in the contemporary usage of "value."[192] The ancients spoke of *virtues* as something knowable and objective that would promote human flourishing. Using "value" in this sense, we can talk of justice, goodness or rightness as being just as real as mountains and gravitation. But today, we tend to focus more on the *psychological* process of evaluation, a process which results in our valuing something. Thus for us a "value" is a subjective, personal possession: it characterizes not how valuable something is, but how much we value it.

As a result, when neuroscientists and evolutionary psychologists provide accounts of the origin of "morality," it is easy for them to confuse two quite different questions.[193] These theories typically try to explain the neuroanatomical[194] features correlated with moral cognition (such as the prefrontal cortex, vital to our self-control) or to suggest an evolutionary origin for the moral sense.[195] But this only looks at values in the subjective, psychological sense: it concerns how and why we tend to *think* and *feel* some things are good

---

[190] For example, see Baker and Goetz, eds., *The Soul Hypothesis*; Moreland, *The Recalcitrant Imago Dei*; David Barnett, "You Are Simple," in Robert C. Koons and George Bealer, eds., *The Waning of Materialism* (New York: Oxford University Press, 2010), 161–174; E. J. Lowe, *Personal Agency: The Metaphysics of Mind and Action* (New York: Oxford University Press, 2008); and Richard Swinburne, *Mind, Brain, and Free Will* (New York: Oxford University Press, 2013).

[191] For an excellent discussion of this point, see Goetz and Taliaferro, *Naturalism*, chapter 2.

[192] A good study of the decline of virtue language is Gertrude Himmelfarb, *The Demoralization of Society: From Victorian Virtues to Modern Values* (New York: Knopf, 1995).

[193] A good example of this confusion is Christopher Boehm's recent book, *The Evolution of Virtue, Altruism, and Shame* (New York: Basic Books, 2012). Boehm's evolutionary account of how humans allegedly came to value things is presented as an account of the evolution of morality, as if actions became good or evil when we came to think of them in a certain way. By contrast, in Scripture, the validity of God's moral law is never made dependent on anyone's recognition of that validity. Indeed whole nations can be wrong, following false gods and mistaken moral and religious beliefs, and God judges them because of their failure to acknowledge His moral law.

[194] Neuroanatomy is that specialized branch of anatomy that studies the various functional components of the human brain and nervous system.

[195] For example, see James Q. Wilson, *The Moral Sense* (New York: The Free Press, 1993); Larry Arnhart's *Darwinian Natural Right* (Albany, NY: State University of New York Press, 1998); and Frans de Waal, *Primates and Philosophers: How Morality Evolved* (Princeton, NJ: Princeton University Press, 2009).

or bad, right or wrong, but it has nothing to do with what actually *is* good or bad, right or wrong.

If by morality we mean a moral law—a system of objectively binding obligations and duties—these accounts have *nothing* to do with morality. These theories at most may tell us something of the secondary causes that have shaped our moral faculties and that play a role in our moral cognition. This by itself tells us nothing about whether or not there is, beyond these secondary causes, an objective moral law according to which some of these thoughts and feelings are correct and some are not. As C. S. Lewis argues, such "an account may (or may not) explain why men do in fact make moral judgments. It does not explain how they could be right in making them."[196]

It is only if the accounts claim to give a sufficient, materialistic account of the moral law itself that they could hope to show that the moral law is not transcendent. But this appears to be a serious case of overreach: materialistic science is equipped to tell us about what is and about what in fact happens, but it cannot tell us what should be or what ought to happen. To claim otherwise is to commit the naturalistic or "is/ought fallacy," where one moves illicitly from what in fact occurs in nature to a conclusion about what ought to occur. In particular, scientific facts about why and how we value certain things cannot tell us whether we should value them. The mere fact that we value something in the psychological sense does not show that it is valuable. For example, a person may psychologically value a poisoned apple as food, but it does not follow that the apple is valuable as nourishment.

So in all of these cases, thoughtful Christians in the sciences should guard against the ideological appropriation of science—the attempt to make science say more than it really can. To the extent that much of science restricts itself to secondary causes within nature, it is incapable of making pronouncements on transcendent matters like God, the soul, and objective moral values. The illusion that it can make such pronouncements often derives from an unconscious commitment to scientism, an ideology often associated with materialism.

b. Scientism

Scientism is a philosophical handmaiden of materialism. While materialism is a metaphysical claim (about what exists), scientism is an epistemological claim (about what we can know). In its strong form, scientism asserts that materialistic science is the only means of *knowing* what is real.[197] Materialists typically claim that science can *only* disclose material causes of material effects. Notice that this is much stronger than saying that most of the

---

[196] C. S. Lewis, *Miracles*, 2d ed. (New York: Macmillan, 1960), 36.

[197] A weaker version of scientism admits that there may be other sources of evidence, but asserts that materialistic science is the most authoritative and hence best source for anything we can confidently call knowledge.

time this is what science does, which is uncontroversial. Still, even if science could never provide evidence for immaterial entities such as God, the soul, and objective moral values, we have just seen that this by itself has no bearing on whether or not these entities exist. Only if this (alleged) fact is combined with scientism in its strong form are we led to conclude that knowledge of such immaterial entities is impossible. If science is the only way to know what is real, and science can only discover the material, then immaterial entities are unknowable.

How should thoughtful Christians respond to such an argument? One response is an in-principle objection: full-strength scientism is internally incoherent, for two reasons. First, scientism is not science—materialistic or otherwise—but a philosophical claim *about* science. If that is so, and materialistic science exhausts what is knowable, then no one can know that scientism is true. Second, even within science, scientific theories require for their formulation the existence of abstract objects like numbers and mathematical relations. Abstract objects, however, are not material objects and (as many philosophers argue) they are not "the sorts of properties whose instances can stand in physical causal relations with the brain."[198] These theories are themselves collections of propositions held to be at least approximately true, and propositions (and arguably, truth itself) also seem to be abstract entities and hence not physical.

If this is right, and if scientism is true, then scientific theories are not themselves knowable because they involve non-materialistic metaphysical commitments. On the other hand, if we can know that a scientific theory is (at least approximately) true, then it must be that we can have knowledge of the non-material entities that are presupposed by stating that theory and by attempting to verify or falsify its claims, in which case scientism is false. But if scientism is rejected and non-physical objects are allowed as potential items of knowledge, then there is no reason to exclude the possibility of knowing God, the soul, and objective moral values.

Another response is an in-fact objection: in fact, it is highly implausible to claim that materialistic science is the only legitimate source of knowledge. Full-strength scientism appears to be an example of intellectual imperialism, in which one discipline attempts to claim a monopoly on knowledge by dele-gitimizing other sources. Yet it is hard for anyone well-versed in great poetry, plays, novels, etc., to believe that none of this literature provides knowledge about the human condition. Similarly, mathematicians and logicians seem to provide knowledge that is not dependent on material causes. For example, Kurt Gödel, Alan Turing, and many other mathematical logicians proved theorems which show that there are some things that no digital computer can

---

[198] Moreland, *The Recalcitrant Imago Dei*, 149.

do.[199] These results hold regardless of how the computer is physically implemented at the hardware level and are not obtained by interacting with actual physical computers—indeed, some of the results preceded the existence of any physical, general purpose digital computer. Thus this knowledge of the limitations of physical systems appears to transcend anything that could be known by interacting with material causes, including physical computers themselves. Also it seems that we know some things—that we are selves, that we can reason, that we have free will and moral responsibility—by introspection, by direct, first-person access to an immaterial mind or soul. We do not know such things by the impersonal observations of materialistic science, such as observations and manipulations of brains. It is hard to read the works of the great ancient and medieval philosophers (such as Plato, Aristotle, Augustine and Aquinas) and deny that they contain any knowledge about the nature of moral virtues and their connection to human flourishing, despite the fact that moral virtues are not materialistic entities.

A third response is a practical objection: if something is true, coherent and important, we would expect it to be possible to live by it. Yet no one can live as if scientism is true. In our ordinary dealings with others, we must generally assume that they are enduring, rational persons with free will and moral responsibility, and we think of ourselves in the same way. If we do not think of people in this way, we can no longer make rational sense of their behavior. Yet enduring, rational, free, moral beings do not seem to be merely material objects. Purely materialistic science gives no evidence of the existence of such beings. So it seems we must assume we can know something about people that we cannot know if scientism is true. Further, even within science, scientists must act as if they know what numbers, truth, consistency, and logical implications are, but abstract objects (like numbers) and relations (like truth, consistency, and logical implication) are not material entities.

Finally, and most important, the thoughtful Christian should reject scientism on scriptural grounds, since it is directly incompatible with the biblical teaching that man has a natural knowledge of God.[200] According to Romans 1:19–20, we can know of God's existence and attributes from studying nature, so our knowledge must not be limited to the physical causes of physical phe-

---

[199] Gödel's first incompleteness theorem shows that for any computer which incorporates the axioms of basic arithmetic, there will be statements true in that system which the computer cannot prove. His second theorem on consistency shows that if the computer is consistent it will not be able to prove that fact. Alan Turing showed that there cannot be a general purpose computer which can tell whether or not an arbitrary computer will ever halt (e.g., it cannot tell whether or not it contains an infinite loop). This is known as the "halting problem." Gödel's paper is available in Jean van Heijenoort, ed., *From Frege to Gödel: A Source Book in Mathematical Logic, 1879–1931*, 3rd ed., (Cambridge, Mass.: Harvard University Press, 1967). Alan Turing's paper, "On Computable Numbers, with an Application to the Entscheidungsproblem (1936)," is in *The Essential Turing: Ideas that Gave Birth to the Computer Age*, B. Jack Copeland, ed. (Oxford: Oxford University Press, 2004).

[200] For a discussion of the reality and limits of the natural knowledge of God, see the CTCR's report on *The Natural Knowledge of God in Christian Confession and Christian Witness*.

nomena. Likewise, Romans 2:14–15 says that everyone can know something of God's moral law, despite its being a transcendent, non-material entity. And Christ himself clearly distinguishes between body and soul and (unless one radically reinterprets the plain meaning of Jesus' words) this makes sense only if both the soul and the body are entities His hearers know about: "And do not fear those who kill the body but cannot kill the soul. Rather fear him who can destroy both soul and body in hell" (Matt. 10:28).[201] Suppose instead that Jesus had distinguished between some undefined X and our body. If Jesus had implied that our X is not the same as our body, and that we should worry about our X as well, this would have conveyed no information because people do not know what their X is. Jesus' actual remarks make sense because people have an innate knowledge or awareness of their souls, despite the fact that souls are not material entities.

It can be concluded that, in its strong form, scientism is directly opposed to an authentically Christian worldview. However, there are many weaker ideologies associated with materialism, and it is often claimed that these at least are compatible with a Christian worldview. There are several related attempts to suggest that Christians can, in effect, think as if they are materialists within the realm of science, even though they are not. Indeed, some people have claimed that the "scientific method" requires Christians to bracket their faith in this way. This view has become quite popular among Christian scientists. The two best-know versions of this strategy are "methodological naturalism" and the idea that science and religion are "non-overlapping magisteria."

c. Methodological naturalism

Philosophical naturalism is the claim that the natural world is all there is. It is possible to be a naturalist and not a materialist, as, for example, some "broad" naturalists[202] believe that souls and objective moral values are part of nature.[203] Yet most naturalists are materialists of some sort (eliminative, reductive, or non-reductive), and for many, "naturalism" and "materialism"

---

[201] There are Christian physicalists (such as Kevin Corcoran, Nancey Murphy, and Trenton Merricks) who claim that human beings are or emerge from physical objects and who deny the existence of an immaterial soul, but it seems they must implausibly claim that Jesus was just using the thought-forms of the time (souls do not really exist, but the "soul" is short-hand for something revealed by modern science), which appears to imply that Jesus was either confused, misleading or simply wrong! Surely, if Jesus is God and knew that the "soul" does not really exist (or reduces to, or wholly depends on the body), he would not have contrasted the body with the soul as if they are two different things.

[202] Goetz and Taliaferro make the distinction between strict and broad naturalism in their book *Naturalism*.

[203] Thus there are atheistic moral Platonists who think that nature includes both physical objects and forces and a realm of moral values or virtues. For example, see Walter Sinnott-Armstrong, *Morality Without God* (New York: Oxford University Press, 2009) and Erik Wielenberg, "In Defense of Non-Natural, Non-Theistic Moral Realism," *Faith and Philosophy* 26:1 (2009), 23–41.

are interchangeable terms. Naturalism still denies that God exists, and if the naturalist is a materialist, he or she will typically deny the existence of the soul and objective moral values as well. However, these exclusions are not required if one embraces only *methodological* naturalism. Methodological naturalism is a rule of scientific method which includes a permission clause and an obligation clause. The permission clause says that scientists may believe in any entities they want, including supernatural entities like God and angels. The obligation clause says that within science, however, scientists must act *as if* naturalism is true (as if there are no supernatural entities).

The posture of methodological naturalism is defended by a number of supporting arguments. Some of these are *a priori* "in principle" arguments, to the effect that science must by its nature be limited to natural causes. Others are *a posteriori* "in fact" arguments, which aim to show that science has been most successful when it has been guided by methodological naturalism. These arguments are advanced by both Christians and non-Christians, but they have also been widely critiqued by both Christians and non-Christians. This suggests a cautious and balanced approach should be taken in discussing the merit of these arguments, one that attempts to hear out the concerns on both sides.

1) In-principle arguments for methodological naturalism

Some of the most common in-principle arguments are designed to show that such immaterial entities as God and the soul cannot be detected by science because science can only discern the existence of entities that behave in predictable ways. The problem with immaterial entities, it is argued, is that if an immaterial God (or the soul) has free will, there is no way for a scientist to control or predict what such a being will do. Therefore, it is claimed, science is better off studying material entities that behave in regular ways.

Thus, for example, Michael Ruse famously argued at the Arkansas creation-science trial of 1981–1982[204] that science can only account for those phenomena produced *in accordance with natural law*. Having free will, neither God nor souls are governed by natural law, and so appealing to these supernatural entities does not qualify as a scientific explanation. Closely connected with Ruse's point are several other concerns. In science, we generally accept a result only if it is *replicable*. The free actions of God or a soul, however, need never be repeated, nor need diverse actions conform to some overarching pattern. For related reasons, some worry that appeal to God or souls is empirically sterile, because it leads to no interesting predictions and because science cannot work with such entities since they are not experimentally controllable. One cannot specify conditions, or design an experiment, such that it

---

[204] See "A Philosopher's Day in Court" and "Witness Testimony Sheet," both in M. Ruse, ed., *But Is It Science? The Philosophical Question in the Creation/Evolution Question* (Buffalo, NY: Prometheus Books, 1988).

is reasonable to expect God or a soul to do something, since they can always choose to do otherwise.

Another set of concerns centers on what counts as a scientific explanation. The worry is that appeal to God or souls is a "science stopper," which commits the "God of the gaps" (or "soul of the gaps") fallacy. The first concern is that if we say that God or a soul did something, there seems nothing more to be said. This would discourage scientists from further investigation of possible causal mechanisms. The second concern is that appeal to God or souls is really an argument from ignorance: it takes the form, *since we do not know how some surprising phenomenon arises, it must be that God or a soul did it.* But from the fact that we do not know a statement to be true, it does not follow that it is false —otherwise, centuries of uncertainty about whether the Earth is moving would imply that it was not. Thus, scientists may urge that our current inability to understand a natural mechanism that could produce a remarkable phenomenon does not mean that no such mechanism will ever be discovered.

All of these arguments have some force, in the sense that there are many areas of science in which the concerns raised make a great deal of sense. This is because much of science is concerned with investigating secondary causes within nature and pursues a paradigm sometimes called *operations science*. In operations science, scientists focus on repeatable and controllable[205] and therefore predictable effects. They are interested in cases where it is possible for us to isolate and analyze a tractable, physical mechanism that accounts for the phenomenon. In this domain, methodological naturalism is, at the least, a very reasonable rule of thumb, because the goal is to discover a natural regularity, one which relates natural causes with natural effects in a predictable way. The underlying logic of operations science is inductive logic, which looks for repeating patterns of causation and infers a general law. This logic can only be used if there are predictable connections between causes and effects, and therefore is unsuited to investigating the free actions of God and souls.

Problems arise, however, if it is claimed that methodological naturalism is (or is part of) a universal scientific method, one that applies in all domains of science. This is mainly because not all of science is operations science. In the *historical science* paradigm, scientists focus on singular (non-repeatable) events. For example, they may investigate the origin of the cosmos, the mass extinction of dinosaurs, a particular volcanic eruption, a crime, or any other historical event which, in all of its specificity, cannot be repeated, even if there are similar events (e.g., other extinctions, volcanic eruptions or crimes of the same sort). There was just one origin of the cosmos, and Abraham Lincoln

---

[205] Of course, scientists do not literally control the orbit of a planet. But it is controllable in the sense that the scientist can reliably specify the conditions which govern the planet's path, so that if those conditions obtain, the orbit is predictable. Operations science requires controllability in addition to repeatability. Even God or souls could repeat the same type of event, but that would not make it any easier to predict their future actions.

was assassinated only once. In historical science, the focus is not repeatable types of events, but particular, singular events. They are not controllable, because there are no conditions under which *those* events could recur. So in these cases, scientists are not looking for a law of nature and do not use inductive logic, since they are not trying to understand the relation between a class of causes and a class of effects, but a singular cause of a singular effect.

Instead, in historical science, scientists investigate the evidential traces surrounding a particular event, consider the range of possible, plausible explanations, and seek to infer the one that is the best current explanation.[206] This turns out to be quite a sophisticated process, but the main idea is that the best current explanation will be the one that not only covers the available data, but also appeals to an entity with the causal powers required to explain it.[207] This leads to a major contrast with operations science. It is to be expected that operations science will center its attention exclusively on the investigation of natural causes of natural effects, so it will operate within methodological naturalism. But in historical science, it appears impossible to justify an *a priori* presumption in favor of natural causes. To be sure, there are many cases where scientists have discovered particular natural causes of particular natural effects (e.g., the plate movements that caused a volcanic eruption). But in the competition for best data coverage and requisite causal power, there is no guarantee that the best candidate explanation will be one appealing solely to natural causes.

This is particularly clear if "natural causes" are defined to include only those undirected causes that feature in the theories of modern, physical science. These causes include events that happen of necessity (as a result of natural law) or by chance (e.g., the decay of a radioactive nucleus), but they exclude the intelligent actions of an agent (such as God or souls). There are several kinds of cases where an intelligent cause seems to be a better explanation of the phenomena than an undirected cause. In some cases, the intelligent cause clearly resides within nature; in other cases, it is plausible that the cause transcends nature, and may even be God, although this usually does not follow from the scientific evidence alone.

Examples of the first kind of case include forensic science, archaeology, cryptography, artificial intelligence, and the Search for Extraterrestrial Intelligence (SETI). For example, when forensic science investigates a fire, it will consider three main kinds of explanation: (1) natural necessity (e.g., the circuits were overloaded and this caused the fire); (2) chance (e.g., while repainting a building, workers accidentally caused contact between worn insulators creating a closed circuit and this caused the fire); or (3) design (e.g., there was a deliberate act of arson). To protect themselves against fraudulent

---

[206] See Carol Cleland, "Methodological and Epistemic Differences between Historical Science and Experimental Science," in *Philosophy of Science*, 69:3 (September 2002), 474–496.

[207] See Peter Lipton, *Inference to the Best Explanation* (New York: Routledge, 2004).

claims, insurance companies hire forensic scientists, and they may sometimes find that there are clear signs of intentional action making design a better explanation than chance or necessity. Similarly, when they discover unusual complex objects, archaeologists use tests to distinguish between the product of natural causes (e.g., a wind sculpture) and the product of design (an artifact such as an arrow head or a tablet inscribed with language). In cryptography, algorithms are applied to a complex signal to see if it is simply meaningless "noise" (a natural product) or if it contains a coherent, coded message (the result of intelligent design). Workers in artificial intelligence (AI) attempt to devise tests to distinguish between intelligent and unintelligent behavior and scientists in the SETI project consider which signals from outer space should convince us that there are other intelligent creatures in the cosmos.

Examples of the second kind include study of the "fine-tuning" of the laws of nature for intelligent life,[208] study of the origin of the information found in all life, and the investigation of miracle claims. In cosmology, scientists have discovered evidence that the particular values of the variables in the fundamental laws of nature are finely tuned to permit intelligent life and even to make effective scientific discovery of those laws possible.[209] In origin of life studies, the natural causes of chance and necessity have proven wholly inadequate to account for the large amount of complex specified information found in all life.[210] And the sheer number of well-attested miracle claims from around the world and throughout the centuries makes it hard to maintain that all of them are based on illusions or fraud.[211]

It is worth pointing out that in neither kind of case is the argument a "gap" argument in the objectionable sense of an argument from ignorance. When scientists infer human (or machine, or alien) intelligence, they do not argue that we do not know what caused some event, therefore an intelligent human (machine, or alien) did it. Scientists do not argue from what we as humans do not know, but from what we do know. We do know that natural causes generally do not produce the evidential traces surrounding some fires, or produce tablets of writing, or messages from space. We do know that intelligent causes (humans, etc.) often produce effects like these. So it is more

---

[208] Defenders of the fine-tuning argument claim that the specific constants governing gravitation, electromagnetism, and the weak and strong nuclear forces fall within a very narrow (and hence improbable) range that permits complex, intelligent life to exist. Thus, it is argued, the values of these constants are "fine-tuned" to enable a specific goal (complex, intelligent life) and this provides evidence that our cosmos is designed to host such life.

[209] See Guillermo Gonzalez and Jay Richards, *The Privileged Planet*. See also Eric Metaxas, "Science Increasingly Makes the Case for God," *The Wall Street Journal*, December 25:2014, online at http://www.wsj.com/articles/eric-metaxas-science-increasingly-makes-the-case-for-god-1419544568.

[210] See Meyer, *Signature in the Cell*.

[211] For the most thorough study to date, see Craig S. Keener, *Miracles: The Credibility of the New Testament Accounts*, 2 vols. (Grand Rapids: Baker Academic, 2011). Despite the subtitle, the book not only reviews the direct evidence for New Testament miracles, but also includes more recent reports from Asia, Africa, and Latin America, and many contemporary examples from the West.

reasonable to think an intelligent cause was responsible than that the effects are just the freak result of undirected causes. The arguments from fine-tuning, the information in life and apparent miracles proceed in just the same way, except that it seems no ordinary agent like a human (or even an alien) could account for the phenomena.

It is indeed open to the naturalist to say that we may find some purely natural cause, but it is an inference to the best explanation that allows for this. It says that intelligence may be the best *current* explanation, given the presently available evidence and the present range of competing explanations. This allows that new evidence or a better theory might come along and cause us to revise our opinion of the best explanation. This shows, however, that the findings of science are fallible and revisable, so it is certainly possible that a design explanation is unseated by new discoveries. But it does not follow that design cannot be the best available explanation given what we currently know.

To be sure, some cautions are in order. Inferring the existence of a super-human, intelligent cause is not the same as inferring that this cause is God. Proponents of Intelligent Design emphasize that further philosophical and theological assumptions are typically required to draw these conclusions. For example, in his book, *The Edge of Evolution*, Behe notes that inferring design from the biological evidence does not by itself license identification of the designer, or imply that the designer is supernatural.

> Like it or not, a raft of important distinctions intervene between a conclusion of design and identification of a designer. The designer need not even be a truly 'supernatural' being.[212]

Likewise, Stephen Meyer argues that a scientific design inference does not establish that the designer is supernatural because it goes beyond what we can claim to know on the basis of our actual experience of finite designers.

> The theory of intelligent design does not claim to detect a super-natural intelligence possessing unlimited powers…. Because the inference to design depends upon our uniform experience of cause and effect in this world, the theory cannot determine whether or not the designing intelligence putatively responsible for life has powers beyond those on display in our experience. Nor can the theory of intelligent design determine whether the intelligent agent responsible for information in life acted from the natural or the 'supernatural' realm. Instead, the theory of intelligent design merely claims to detect the action of some *intelligent* cause …. The theory of intelligent design does not claim to be able to determine the identity or any other attributes of that intelligence, even if philosophical deliberation or

---

[212] Michael Behe, *The Edge of Evolution: The Search for the Limits of Darwinism* (New York: Free Press, 2007), 228.

additional evidence from other disciplines may provide reasons to consider, for example, a specifically theistic design hypothesis.[213]

So, while the design inference could be supplemented with other considerations (further data and background philosophical and theological arguments and theories) to produce an argument for a supernatural deity, this would go beyond the modest contribution of the design inference to science.

This caution is borne out by the unsurprising fact that naturalistic scientists and philosophers and their critics disagree about the proper explanation of apparent design in nature. In the case of apparently transcendent design (such as fine-tuning, the origin of the information in life, and miracles), naturalists attempt to show that the appearance of design is an illusion, while their opponents argue that the design is real.[214] Thus, for example, the claim that physical constants are finely-tuned to permit intelligent life is countered with the suggestion that ours is but one of many universes in a multiverse, and if there are enough universes, it is not so surprising that at least some support intelligent life. In response, defenders of fine-tuning point out that these other universes are necessarily unobservable and appear to violate Occam's razor[215] (a single creator is a simpler hypothesis).

The claim that the information in life is a signature of intelligence has been countered by the proposal that natural properties are capable of spontaneously self-organizing into systems of greater and greater complexity, eventually resulting in life. In response, defenders of design have pointed out that known cases of self-organization produce repeating (periodic) structures, like crystals, but the assembly instructions for molecular machines and organs require highly aperiodic information.

Miracle claims are usually countered by some version of Hume's two classic arguments: either we can never, even in principle, have good reason to accept a miracle claim, or in fact there are no credible miracle claims. In response, defenders of miracles have argued that Hume's in-principle argument makes serious errors in logic,[216] and as Keener has shown, his in-fact argument is simply mistaken.[217]

---

[213] Meyer, *Signature in the Cell*, 428–429.

[214] See for example the exchange between philosopher of physics Robin Collins, who defends the fine-tuning design argument, and atheist physicist Victor Stenger who attempts to debunk the argument in J. P. Moreland, Chad Meister, and Khaldoun Sweis, eds., *Debating Christian Theism* (New York: Oxford University Press, 2013).

[215] See chapter 1, p. 39.

[216] See John Earman, *Hume's Abject Failure: The Argument Against Miracles* (Oxford: Oxford University Press, 2000). Earman shows that Hume's argument confuses the inductive probability appropriate for establishing laws of nature with the kind of probability relevant to establishing singular historical events.

[217] Keener, *Miracles*, focuses chapters 5 and 6 on explicitly responding to Hume, but the whole work provides extensive historical and contemporary evidence of reliably attested miracles.

The same dialectic is operative where the intelligent cause operates wholly within nature. Thus naturalistic philosophers have attempted to argue that human intelligence can itself be accounted for by purely natural causes, in either a reductive or non-reductive scheme. But there is an increasing number of sophisticated arguments to show that this project is not feasible. Intelligent agents are characterized by such remarkable features as consciousness, intentionality, and rationality, and philosophers have provided rigorous arguments that appear to demonstrate that none of these features can be explained naturalistically.[218]

The important point is that these controversies about the proper interpretation of the data do nothing to show that inferring an intelligent cause is unscientific. On a given occasion, such an inference may be mistaken, or it may be shown to be mistaken later, but the same is true of scientific inferences in general. Many naturalistic inferences have been discredited (e.g., the claim that comets are atmospheric phenomena, that planetary orbits are the result of compound circular motion, that marsh gas causes malaria, that electromagnetic radiation is propagated by an invisible ether, etc.), but that does not mean they were unscientific. Further, while a design inference alone does not show that an intelligent cause is a supernatural being like God, and while such arguments that typically rely on additional theological and philosophical assumptions, it is not clear that there are *no* cases in which a sufficient range of scientific facts is best explained by a supernatural cause. Both the origin of the universe and the fine-tuning of the laws of nature seem poorly explained by any cause (intelligent or otherwise) within nature, since these signs of design pervade all of nature. And some remarkable, well-attested phenomena recorded in miracle claims also seem to require a supernatural explanation. So, methodological naturalism does not seem defensible as a universal requirement for every domain of science.

As many philosophers have argued, dogmatic adherence to methodological naturalism appears both to be "question-begging"[219] and to risk delinking science from its primary function of finding the truth about the natural world.[220] The underlying principle of methodological naturalism begs the question because if we assert that science should only ever infer natural causes, then we have already assumed that there can be no scientific evidence of supernatural causes. While there are many cases where it is reasonable only

---

[218] See, for example, Angus Menuge, *Agents Under Fire: Materialism and the Rationality of Science* (Lanham, MD: Rowman and Littlefield, 2004), and J. P. Moreland, *The Recalcitrant Imago Dei*.

[219] See Robert Larmer, "Is Methodological Naturalism Question-Begging?" *Philosophia Christi* 5 (2003), 113–130.

[220] See Bradley Monton, *Seeking God in Science: An Atheist Defends Intelligent Design* (Boulder, CO: Broadview Press, 2009); Steve Dilley, "Philosophical Naturalism and Methodological Naturalism: Strange Bedfellows?" *Philosophia Christi* 12 (2010), 118–141; Angus Menuge, "Against Methodological Materialism," in Bealer and Koons, eds.,*The Waning of Materialism*, 375–394.

to expect a natural causal explanation, some phenomena (e.g., fine-tuning, biological information, miracles) seem to resist such explanation, and it seems odd to suggest that science could not, even in principle, conclude that the best explanation of these phenomena is a supernatural cause. Further, asserting that science could never say this means that science can no longer claim to be a no-holds-barred attempt to gain knowledge of the world. After all, "science" means knowledge, and it is hard to see why the discovery that some phenomena are best explained by a supernatural cause does not qualify as something scientists could know. Why should science truncate its inquiry so that it only considers natural causes, instead of following the evidence wherever it leads?

In fact, if it is taken as a universal, *a priori* principle of science, methodological naturalism appears to be an irrational rule, as can be brought out by analogies. Suppose one drops one's car keys at night, but decides to look for them only in the light of the street lamps, because one is afraid of the dark and it is harder to see. This provides no evidence that the keys are not lying in the dark. Or suppose a pirate with a map goes to an island to find buried treasure, and decides to search every region of the island except the one marked "Here there be dragons." This provides no evidence that the treasure is not to be found where the alleged dragons are located. In general, refusing in principle to consider some kinds of causes provides no reason to think that they are not the true causes, or that the evidence does not point most strongly to those causes.

2) In-fact arguments for methodological naturalism

Quite a few defenders of methodological naturalism admit that there is no way to establish the principle on *a priori* grounds. Instead, they content themselves with the *a posteriori* argument that, as a matter of fact, excluding the supernatural from science has proven very fruitful for scientific discoveries.[221] As we saw in the previous chapter, Bacon, Descartes, Hobbes, and Galileo all attacked the idea of design in the form of Aristotelian final causes. It can be argued that science has been very successful in many areas by only considering undirected causes operating wholly within nature. If science has had so much success ignoring intelligent causes, why should it remain open to discovering them?

The problem with this argument is that it is easy to explain why science obedient to methodological naturalism has been successful in some areas without taking this as evidence that it is a sound, general principle. As we saw earlier, when we are investigating the proximal, secondary causes of physical events, there is generally no reason to expect an intelligent cause (finite or supernatural). Since, for many people, this kind of "operations science" dominates their conception of what science is, it is not surprising if they con-

---

[221] See, for example, Patrick McDonald and Nivaldo J. Tro, "In Defense of Methodological Naturalism," *Christian Scholar's Review* 38: 2 (2009), 201–229.

clude that methodological naturalism is a sensible rule. But as we also saw, historical science, by its nature, has to be open to intelligent causes: there is no way to rule out the possibility that the intelligent choice of a human, machine, alien, or transcendent being is the best explanation of a historical event. And, as philosopher of science Del Ratzsch has argued, to make the case that an intelligent cause of a historical event is supernatural, all one would have to do is provide evidence that none of the finite intelligences within nature is causally adequate to account for that event:

> If unaided nature cannot generate some phenomenon, and there that phenomenon is in front of us, then obviously some other agency was involved. If we add the premise that humans couldn't or didn't produce the phenomenon, whereas aliens could have, we get the aliens-of-the-gaps arguments, which is precisely what underlies SETI. If we add the further premise that aliens couldn't or didn't ... then supernatural agency follows.[222]

Further, there are a number of historical facts about the universe that continue to resist the best naturalistic explanations, such as the ultimate origin of the universe, its fine-tuning for intelligent life and observation, the origin of biological life, the emergence of consciousness and of beings capable of grasping objective moral values. So it is not true that *all* of science provides *a posteriori* evidence of the soundness of methodological naturalism. Rather, our total evidence suggests a more modest conclusion: *methodological naturalism is a reasonable rule of thumb in some areas of science.* Obviously, this modest conclusion is compatible with the existence of good evidence for supernatural design in *other* areas of science.

At this point, some are likely to protest that scientists can simply maintain that any remarkable phenomenon is most likely the result of unknown natural causes. The problem with this response is that it misunderstands the logic used in historical science. As we saw earlier, in historical science scientists use a method of abductive logic (or inference to the best explanation) which examines the evidential traces surrounding a historical event and infers the *best current explanation.* What this means is that the inference is made in light of currently available data and theories. This inference may, of course, be upset by the discovery of new data or by the proposal of new theories, so abductive inference is unstable: today's best explanation may not be the best tomorrow. However, the claim that an unknown natural cause is the best explanation is an illicit appeal to possible, future evidence, not to evidence that we actually have. It is, in effect, "promissory naturalism": it issues a promissory note that there will be a natural explanation sometime in the future. Since science must confine itself to the data and available explanations

---

[222] Del Ratzsch, *Nature, Design and Science: The Status of Design in Natural Science* (Albany, NY: SUNY Press, 2001), 119.

it has, promissory naturalism is not part of a legitimate scientific attitude. Instead, it serves to immunize naturalism from the scientific data that would count against it. Surely, however, the main goal of science is to find the truth about the natural world, not to protect a preconceived philosophical idea (naturalism) from embarrassing data.

To conclude, it seems that one can make a strong case for methodological naturalism as a useful and successful rule of thumb in many areas of science, but neither *a priori* nor *a posteriori* arguments are sufficient to show that it is a universally valid principle. Thoughtful Christians who hope to present scientific evidence to support their claim of faith that we live in a designed world in which God also intervenes should not be deterred by methodological naturalism from making that case. They are well-advised to distinguish clearly between primary and secondary causes and between operations science and historical science, and to focus their argument on examples where there is no reasonable way to exclude the possibility of a supernatural, intelligent cause.

d. The NOMA model of science and theology

Closely related to methodological naturalism are attempts to put science and religion in watertight compartments. Thus the late paleontologist and popular science columnist Stephen Jay Gould claimed that science and religion should be regarded as belonging to "non-overlapping magisteria" (or NOMA for short).[223] Gould borrows the term "magisteria" from the Catholic Church, in which it means a sphere of teaching authority. His suggestion follows the claim, widely attributed to Galileo, that the Holy Spirit's intention in inspiring Scripture was to tell us how we go to heaven, not to tell us how the heavens go.[224] If this dictum is true, and the teaching of the church rests on biblical revelation, then its seems reasonable to claim that the church's proper sphere of authority is to tell mankind how it is saved, not to tell us how the natural world works. If so, it seems reasonable that science is the sole proper authority in the latter domain.

As critics have pointed out, however, an absolute divide between science and religion seems to be unfaithful to the goals of both biblical theology and science. If religion can say nothing authoritative about the natural world, then there is no such thing as natural knowledge of God—contrary to Romans 1 and 2. Moreover, we lose the fact that the Gospel itself makes historical claims—claims about what God in Christ did (and does) within ordinary history, claims that are in principle amenable to investigation by historical science. We know from Scripture that our cosmos and everything in it form a coherent reality because they are all the creations of Christ (Col. 1:16) in

---

[223] See Stephen Jay Gould, *Rock of Ages*, and his "Nonoverlapping Magisteria," *Natural History*, 16–22, 60–62.

[224] For brief discussion over the historical question of whether Galileo was the origin of this dictum, see Edoardo Aldo Cerrato, "How to go to Heaven, and not how the heavens go," available online at: http://www.oratoriosanfilippo.org/galileo-baronio-english.pdf.

whom all things hold together. The creation is vital to the Gospel because it sets forth God's original will for mankind as beings made specially in His image, who by nature feared, loved, and trusted Him above all things. Since we fell from that state, losing original righteousness, God's redemptive work is to heal us and restore us so that we may become the people He originally intended us to be. Without these facts about our creation, Christ's redemptive work makes no sense: we cannot be restored to our originally intended state if we are unintended accidents of an indifferent cosmos. Most scandalous of all, Paul himself says that our faith is founded on the fact of the resurrection, and that if there were no such fact, our faith would be futile (I Cor. 15:17). He makes it clear on numerous occasions that the resurrection was a fact of public history and that there was objective evidence to support it. So it appears that Gould is implicitly siding with those theologians like Karl Barth (1886–1968) who deny any role for natural theology and evidential apologetics. Gould also seems wrong about the domain of science: in principle, historical science could produce evidence that counts for or against the facticity of the resurrection.

In practice, as well, NOMA seems to be disingenuous, because while religion is told that it can make no cognitive (knowledge) claims about the natural world (i.e., it has no authority to make statements with scientific implications), this did not prevent Gould from making claims in the name of science which do have religious implications. Thus Gould asserts that human beings are "a wildly improbable evolutionary event, and not the nub of universal purpose … We are the offspring of history, and must establish our own paths."[225]

This is a statement loaded with religious significance: it claims that science has established that we are not the intended creations of God, that we are not here on earth for a divine purpose and that we do not have divine vocations that define the meaning of life. Rather, we must simply make up our own meanings. So apparently, while religion is prevented from making any claim with scientific implications, science can refute the religious claim of orthodox Christians that human beings are specially made in the image of God to be stewards of the natural world and to carry out the vocations that God prepared in advance for us to do (Eph. 2:10).

As developed by Gould, science includes not only the data and theories we would expect, but also philosophical interpretations which are anything but religiously neutral. So NOMA is really a misnomer. What Gould actually believes in is a *one-way overlapping magisteria* (OOMA): there is overlap from science into religion, but not from religion to science. In other words, while Gould officially portrays science and religion as separate but equal—or complementary—he is actually advancing a scientific imperialist model. According to this model science can continue to make inroads undermining

---

[225] Gould, *Rock of Ages*, 206–207.

and supplanting the claims of religion, while religion is barred from defending itself or from making any critique of scientific overreach.

The sleight of hand that allows this double standard occurs because although it seems that religion is generously being offered autonomy in matters of ultimate or eternal significance, in fact it is not. Religion can talk about these matters so long as it does not make cognitive claims about objective reality, since that is the domain of science. But the fact is, religion does make claims about objective reality which are contrary to those of scientific materialism (it says we were specially created for a purpose, etc.). If religion is prevented from making these claims, it is reduced to a collection of subjective opinions and feelings about reality. One cannot claim that religion is a complementary domain of truth and then prevent it from saying anything that could be true.

e. Science and parascience

Gould's approach is only an example of a much broader tendency to promote the cultural dominance of science. Marilynne Robinson shows that in the attempt to supplant religion with science as the most authoritative source of knowledge, some have conflated science proper with what she calls "parascience." Robinson notes that parascientific literature "makes its case by proceeding, using the science of its moment, from a genesis of human nature in primordial life to a set of general conclusions about what our nature is and must be"[226] In the process, Robinson argues, parascience commits two main fallacies. For one thing, it fallaciously treats current science as ultimate truth when, at best, it reflects only the latest, fallible theory. The shortcomings of such a theory could be shown tomorrow by new data or a more comprehensive competitor theory. It also moves from mere descriptions of natural fact to normative conclusions about the way things should be. In this way, for example, evolutionary ethicists claim to have discovered the historical origins of moral norms, confusing a scientific account of the origin of our moral judgments and feelings with an ultimate account of the origin and authority of moral norms.

This imperialist strategy leads its proponents to "deny the reality of phenomena it cannot accommodate, or to scold them for their irksome, atavistic persistence."[227] For example, consciousness, authentic altruism, and religious experience are all either denied or explained away as illusions or delusions. There is a lack of open-minded investigation into these phenomena on their own terms: they have been judged problematic before that investigation begins. An important implication for Christian scientists is to distinguish carefully between the scientific data and scientific models themselves and

---

[226] Marilynne Robinson, *Absence of Mind: The Dispelling of Inwardness from the Modern Myth of the Self* (New Haven: Yale University Press, 2010), 32–33.

[227] Ibid., 72.

agenda-driven philosophical interpretations of those data and models which aim to compel concessions to a non-Christian worldview.

3. Philosophical contributions of Christianity to science

Christians should not only be on their guard against philosophies which attempt to appropriate the name and authority of science to advance their cause. They should also be ready to point out that Christianity is philosophically friendly to science because it provides some key principles that support the scientific enterprise. These principles fall into three broad categories: metaphysical, epistemological, and moral.

a. Metaphysical support for science

If science is conceived as the attempt to comprehend the natural world and critically depends on the discovery of universal laws of nature, then science assumes that nature is fundamentally rational. This assumption is not justified if nature is governed by many gods or local spirits as in polytheistic mythologies or animism. Neither is it justified by the assumption that the universe is simply a brute fact, an inexplicable accident. Furthermore, the vast success of science has shown that the assumption of a rational universe is a highly plausible one. The question which remains is: which worldview best justifies this assumption? Albert Einstein, who was neither a Christian nor an orthodox Jew, hints at the religious implications of these facts in a letter which reflects on the amazing fact that we can discover universal laws of nature. As noted earlier, he writes that

> But *a priori* one should expect a chaotic world which cannot be grasped by the mind in any way ... [T]he kind of order created by Newton's theory of gravitation ... is wholly different. Even if the axioms of the theory are proposed by man, the success of such a project presupposes a high degree of ordering of the objective world .... That is the "miracle" which is being constantly reinforced as our knowledge expands.[228]

Together with other monotheists, Christians can point out that a good explanation of such a coherent, law-governed world is the existence of a single, rational, divine creator. Indeed, the whole idea of a universal law of nature is derived from the prior idea of a single, rational legislator, and if these laws apply throughout nature, then that legislator must be a supernatural being.

Theism thus provides metaphysical support for science by affirming that there is a natural order to discover. Without this assumption, as Einstein realized, science as we understand it today simply is not a feasible project.

---

[228] Albert Einstein, *Letters to Solovine*, 131; also quoted earlier on pages 38–39.

However, an orderly world is not enough for science to be feasible. For it could certainly happen that the world is rational but human beings are not. Here, biblical theism has a decisive advantage because it asserts not only the creation of a law-governed world but also the creation of humans specially made in the image of God with the gifts required to be stewards of that world. This surely predicts that we are sufficiently rational to discern what is going on in nature.

b. Epistemological support for science

This metaphysical claim is the foundation for biblical theism's epistemological support for science. It is not merely that the world is rational and so are we, for that still might not be enough for science to be feasible. It might be that we are simply too limited in our rationality, or that our type of rationality is not attuned to the rationality governing nature. This could happen, for example, if God only provided us with the ability to discover local rules of thumb, but not the universal rules governing the cosmos as a whole. Lying behind the feasibility of science is the fact that one and the same logos (principle of rationality) is supremely exemplified in the mind of God. Thus it is imaged both in the natural world and the human mind, so that human reason is attuned to the rationality of nature and sufficient to discover its principles.

This confidence in our ability to discover the truth about the natural world encourages scientific work. Realistically, however, it is also balanced by a recognition of our creaturely limits and sin. We can conceive the idea of a universal law of nature, and yet our actual theories appear to capture only fallible approximations. We know that God's will and His ways are above our will and our ways, so we must take care to see what He has done rather than anticipate what we think He would do or assume that our ideas are better than His. Even then we can expect that our best efforts to interpret His work will still fall short. As Nathan Jastram has argued,[229] being made like God, and yet not being God, gives just the right balance of confidence and humility so that we are sure science can progress without expecting final answers.

By contrast, it is fascinating to see that contemporary naturalists lurch between the extremes of excessive confidence and excessive humility. When they want to use science as a weapon to attack religion, they are often tempted into the parascience critiqued by Marilynne Robinson, fallaciously converting the temporal and contingent results of science into pronouncements on the ultimate meaning of life. But when they reflect soberly on the consequences of a naturalistic theory of man, they often conclude that we are not truth-oriented creatures, failing to see that this undercuts our confidence in the science alleged to have that consequence. Long ago, Lewis called attention to the self-defeating nature of "scientific" arguments that undermine our confidence in human rationality:

---

[229] Nathan Jastram, "Scientists Called to Be Like God," in Menuge, ed., *Reading God's World*, 243–269.

After studying his environment man has begun to study himself. Up to that point, he had assumed his own reason and through it seen all other things. Now, his reason has become the object: it is as if we took out our eyes to look at them. Thus studied, his own reason appears to him as the epiphenomenon which accompanies chemical or electrical events in a cortex which is itself the by-product of a blind evolutionary process. His own logic, hitherto the king whom events in all possible worlds must obey, becomes merely subjective. There is no reason for supposing that it yields truth.[230]

The severity of this problem does not seem to be recognized by leading evolutionary psychologists. For example, Steven Pinker admits that in his view, "our brains were shaped for fitness, not for truth."[231] Lewis Wolpert claims that "our brains contain a belief generating machine, an engine that can produce beliefs with little relation to what is actually true."[232] With no sense of irony, Wolpert later claims that "Science provides by far the most reliable method for determining whether one's beliefs are valid."[233] The problem, of course, is that if our belief-forming mechanism favors useful but largely false beliefs, this will also include our scientific beliefs. And even if natural selection could somehow hone beliefs relevant to our everyday survival so that *they* were mostly true, this still would not be good grounds to trust recent scientific theories, because they played no role in the survival of our ancestors. In fact, Steven Pinker emphasizes that recent scientific advances solve problems that our ancestors never encountered.

> Our ancestors encountered certain problems for hundreds of thousands or millions of years—recognizing objects, making tools, learning the local language, finding a mate, predicting an animal's movement, finding their way—and encountered certain other problems never—putting a man on the moon ... proving Fermat's last theorem.[234]

The problem-solving abilities of our ancestors give no reason for confidence in our ability to solve scientific problems that go far beyond the requirements of survival. It seems that the prediction of naturalistic evolution is that human beings would have too limited and parochial a grasp of rationality to account for the discovery of universal laws of nature. And of course, we did put a man on the moon.

---

[230] C. S. Lewis, "The Poison of Subjectivism," in Walter Hooper, ed., *Christian Reflections* (London: Fount, 1991), 98.

[231] Steven Pinker, *How the Mind Works* (New York: W.W. Norton and Company, 1997), 305.

[232] Lewis Wolpert, *Six Impossible Things Before Breakfast* (New York: W.W. Norton and Company, 2007), 140.

[233] Ibid., 216.

[234] Pinker, *How the Mind Works*, 304.

c. Moral support for science

The Bible provides several foundational moral parameters for science. It gives reasons to think that we are *permitted* to do science—because nature is not sacred—and we are *required* to do science—as it is part of what it means to pursue our vocations as stewards of creation. Furthermore, as with all legitimate vocations, science was instituted as a means of loving and serving our neighbors, and God provides for our neighbors in part through the work of scientists. This means that so long as we are using science to serve our neighbor's needs in a way that is compatible with our stewardship obligation to preserve the Lord's world as a trust for future generations, we *should* do science. But it also means that God provides boundaries for legitimate science: it must not be used to harm others or the environment in such a way that it harms the welfare of future generations.

Thus again, there is the need for a right balance of confidence and humility. Scripture demonstrates that science can be a God-pleasing vocation! And yet, through His teaching about the purpose of vocation as a means of loving and serving our neighbor, God also reminds us of our responsibilities not to use scientific knowledge and techniques in ways that violate the moral laws that govern all vocations.

4. Conclusion

We have seen that, clustered around materialism, there are a number of philosophical ideas often associated with science which create difficulties for the Christian scientist. This chapter has attempted to explain these ideas and to offer some strategies for effective response. Thoughtful Christians need to gain the critical distance to evaluate the strengths and weaknesses of these ideas for those intent on pursuing science as a vocation. In particular they should not allow themselves to be taken captive by some worldly philosophy (Col. 2:8), such as some version of materialism that biases the empirical method and encourages the thought that God's actions in the world cannot be known. We also briefly noted ways in which the Bible offers foundational assumptions about reality which are friendly to the work of scientists. It should be clear that faithful Christians are above all concerned about *Truth*. They seek and highly value the whole truth revealed in God's Word *and* the whole truth revealed in God's world, and should be vigilant for any attempt to define or use science to ignore or undermine God's revelation. With both eyes open, Christians should do their very best to embrace all the truth He has revealed to us. This requires a sound reading of both Scripture and the scientific data—which is the subject of the following chapter.

Chapter IV

Biblical Knowledge and Scientific Knowledge

1. Introduction

The purpose of this chapter is to consider how we know specific things as Christians and to consider whether there is a genuine conflict between what we know from Scripture and what we know from modern science. We will begin by comparing the kind of knowing that is critical for science and the unique sort of knowing that is central to Christianity (section 2). In section 3 we will identify important principles for knowing (understanding) what the Scripture means, and then we will consider how these basic principles of scriptural interpretation can help us to handle apparent conflicts between science and Scripture while upholding the final authority of God's Word. In section 4 we will explore more deeply some examples where biblical and scientific truth claims seem to conflict.

2. Knowing as a Christian

Consider the meaning of "we know" in the following statements from earlier in this document.

- "We now **know** that Kepler's 'laws' are only approximations to the truth."[235]

- "And it seems we **know** some things ... by introspection, by direct, first-person access to an immaterial mind or soul, not via the impersonal observations of materialistic science, such as observations and manipulations of brains."[236]

- "We do **know** that natural causes generally do not produce the evidential traces surrounding some fires, or produce tablets of writing, or messages from space. We do **know** that intelligent causes (humans, etc.) often do produce effects like these."[237]

- "We **know** from Scripture that our cosmos and everything in it form a coherent reality because they are all the creations of Christ

---

[235] Chapter 1, p. 49. Emphasis added.

[236] Chapter 3, p. 80. Emphasis added.

[237] Chapter 3, p. 85. Emphasis added.

(Col. 1:16) in whom all things hold together."[238]

- "We **know** that God's will and His ways are above our will and our ways."[239]

We may often speak of "knowing" things that we learn from science and "believing" things that we learn from the Bible. As the statements above show, however, we can just as easily speak of knowing things like the will of God and the identity of the Creator as we can speak of knowing things like astronomical theories or the difference between human writing and naturally produced marks on a piece of wood or stone. There are very real similarities between knowing things that we learn from each of "God's books," His Word and His works in nature.

Perhaps the most immediately apparent similarity is that whether learning from God's Word or His works, an interpreter is confronted by data. Whether it is written words in a text or the results of scientific experimentation, both the reader of Scripture and the scientist are interpreting information that confronts them. Each must analyze, distinguish, separate, categorize, and arrange the data in ways that will prove meaningful to himself and—hopefully—to others.[240]

The use of prior knowledge is another common feature of knowing things based on God's Word and His works. In both cases the interpreter makes use of what he or she already knows while studying this new "data set." Reading Scripture requires knowing vocabulary, grammar, syntax, and more, just as the scientist uses prior knowledge of his field.[241]

A third common feature is that in both cases the way questions are framed will have an important impact on the answers that are discovered. Chapter 3 pointed out that scientism may boast of answers to questions concerning the

---

[238] Chapter 3, pages 91–92. Emphasis added.

[239] Chapter 3, p. 95. Emphasis added.

[240] Our interpretation of data involves assessing the veracity of information we receive on a daily basis and determining whether or not (or to what degree) we can trust that data. Satiric publications such as "The Onion" are not intended to be taken literally but rather to be read as humor—so interpretation of data also involves taking into account factors such as literary genre, contextual issues, and authorial intent. As we continually assess events in the world around us, events that repeat themselves are often "trusted" to recur again (i.e., we "trust" that the sun will rise each day, since it has done so every day of our lives). We also look to the sources of information and are typically more inclined to trust those who are recognized as authorities in various fields of expertise and experience, such as doctors, lawyers, police, teachers, and pastors. In science, measures such as the impact factor of a journal help assessing the degree to which certain studies and conclusions are trusted and deemed to be reliable. Doubt and distrust of published conclusions occur when researchers are unable to repeat or confirm what has been published by others, or when evidence to the contrary is presented—in essence "debunking" the original research.

[241] For an excellent example of how similar these two processes are, see Giovanni Manetti, *Theories of the Sign in Classical Antiquity*, trans. C. Richardson (Bloomington: Indiana University Press, 1993); see especially pages 36–52.

existence of God, even though that question was not addressed (or capable of being addressed) by the research claimed as the basis for denying His existence.[242] Bible readers are also vulnerable to such misunderstandings. We need mention here only those who take up the Revelation of John looking for indications of the precise date of Christ's return. We might say that Luther's breakthrough as a reader of the Bible came when he allowed the text to reframe the questions for him. Rather than reading the Bible as difficult-to-the-point-of-impossible guidance for the sinner desiring to appease an angry god, Luther began to read it as the account of how God was in Christ Jesus reconciling the world to Himself.

A fourth feature was once readily accepted by almost everyone in both the sciences and theology. We earlier referred to the relationship between "God's 'Two Books.'"[243] To speak of God's Word and His works as "books" was a reminder to the "reader" that each of these "books" had the same Author and that *His* truth should be sought in reading *both* of them. Readers of both "books" would have agreed that God's Word and world share a common source and intention.

Such common ground no longer exists, however. Peter Harrison's conclusion seems to describe quite accurately the situation we now face:

> Indeed, that there is now such a disparity between our approaches to words and things, that scientific and literary activities have become so alien to each other, that the 'two cultures' share increasingly less common ground, is owing largely to the break-down of that universal hermeneutics which, in premodern times, had informed the study of both the book of scripture and the book of nature. The transformations which brought on the birth of modernity moved western culture from the era of 'the two books' to that of 'the two cultures.'[244]

The "two cultures" are viewed as largely incompatible by many. At best they are viewed as "non-overlapping magisteria,"[245] and at worst as flatly contradictory or even combative.

Where do we go from here as Christians? Do we cede to science the authority to trump any biblical claim except those that are the most narrowly "spiritual"? Does science "get the last word" as to what humanity can *really* know?

---

[242] See above, chapter 3, 76–78.

[243] Chapter 1, 20–25.

[244] Peter Harrison, *The Bible, Protestantism, and the Rise of Natural Science*, 267. The concept of "two cultures" builds on the discussion initiated by C. P. Snow, *The Two Cultures* (London: Cambridge University Press, 1959), whose concerns are briefly discussed in the introduction of this report on p. 1–3.

[245] See above, chapter 3, 91–93.

Such questions lead us to consider one more example of knowing, this one from the New Testament:

> Indeed, I count everything as loss because of the surpassing worth of **knowing** Christ Jesus my Lord. For his sake I have suffered the loss of all things and count them as rubbish, in order that I may gain Christ and be found in him, not having a righteousness of my own that comes from the law, but that which comes through faith in Christ, the righteousness from God that depends on faith—that I may **know** him and the power of his resurrection, and may share his sufferings, becoming like him in his death, that by any means possible I may attain the resurrection from the dead. (Phil. 3:8–11; emphasis added)

The apostle Paul writes here of knowing some*one*, a *person*—Christ Jesus—as his Lord (v. 8) and receiving from Him a new righteousness unlike his own (righteousness by faith rather than from law; v. 9).[246] Moreover, he seeks to know Christ in a way that includes knowing His power and being made like Him. To know Christ in this way, says Paul, causes a re-valuing of everything else: from Paul's possessions to his understanding of his own capabilities to his willingness to accept suffering. This intimate knowledge of Christ is of supreme value for the apostle.

We should recognize that this type of knowing is of paramount importance not only for Paul, but for Christianity as a whole. This document argues rationally (that is, on the basis of reason) against scientism's biased claim to be the final arbiter of all knowledge. At the same time, however, it is important to confess that *reason or rational arguments are not the ultimate basis for the knowing that Christianity claims for itself.* Rather, Christians *know* that the wisdom of God confounds all human wisdom (1 Cor. 3:19). How do we *know* this? These truths flow out of *knowing* Christ Jesus, who is God's very truth made flesh (John 1:14), God in the nature of a man (Phil. 2:6; Heb. 1:3), and the very wisdom of God (1 Cor. 1:24).

So, although Christianity values reason highly, it recognizes that "it ought not be praised at Christ's expense."[247] Indeed as beneficial as reason can be,

---

[246] Such knowing reflects the fact that the verb "to know," in both its primary Greek (*ginosko*) and Hebrew (*yada*) forms, can have both a more personal dimension and also one that is more narrowly intellectual. (Spanish and some other languages use different verbs to express these two dimensions.) Scripture frequently emphasizes the personal sense. For example, consider its use in Exodus 5:2. "But Pharaoh said, 'Who is the LORD, that I should obey his voice and let Israel go? I do not *know* the LORD, and moreover, I will not let Israel go.'" Here the word "know" signifies the intimate knowledge of a relationship. Certainly Pharaoh was acquainted with basic assertions about Israel's God. He rejected those assertions and also what they would require of him. So also Jesus—whose omniscience enables Him to know all things—says in Matthew 7:21–23 of "workers of lawlessness," "I never *knew* you." A saving, intimate relationship had not been established. These negative examples are contrasted with the same positive use of "know" in Philippians 3.

[247] Ap IV, 24. KW 124.

it is necessary to declare with Martin Luther that it is "pure error" to say that human beings possess "sound reason and a good will."[248] Christianity teaches that in a fallen world, where reason is corrupted, there is no more certain knowledge than to know Christ by faith. Moreover, the Christian faith recognizes that knowing Christ rightly can be done not by human imagination—for that is just as fallible as human reason is—but only by reading the only source of certain truth about Him, the prophetic and apostolic Scriptures.[249] Both the clarity and authority of God's Word, centered in Christ and the Gospel (Luke 24:44–48), exceed God's book of the world.[250] Christ Himself affirms the truth of the Bible which testifies to Him when He assures us, first, that the Hebrew Scriptures (Old Testament) which He heard and fulfilled were entirely trustworthy, even in seemingly little details, for their authors are men "to whom the word of God came—and Scripture cannot be broken" (John 10:35).[251] He then further assures His apostles, whose eyewitness testimony is the foundation of all the New Testament Scriptures, that His Spirit would ensure their witness to Him (John 14:26).

Therefore, as certainly as Christians hold to Christ, knowing Him as their Savior and Lord, with equal certainty they also hold to the Scriptures of the Old and New Testament, knowing them to be the Word of God. We hold fast to the Scriptures as we hold to Christ, knowing that in them we have the testimony not only of men, but also God's own Word and His *supernatural revelation* that makes Christ known and is "profitable" for all teaching (2 Tim. 3:15–17). Therefore it is important to state clearly that even as the church *confesses its faith in Christ,* so also its conviction of the complete trustworthiness of the Holy Scriptures is a confession of faith. As the CTCR expresses it elsewhere:

> Even though there are differences and variety in the Sacred Writings which sometimes perplex us because we can find no harmonization for them that satisfies human reason, faith confesses the Bible to be the inerrant Word of God. Since the inerrancy of the Scriptures is a matter of faith, it is by definition

---

[248] SA III.1.4; KW 311. A more detailed discussion of Luther's thoughts about human reason can be found in B. A. Gerrish, *Grace and Reason: A Study in the Theology of Luther* (Eugene, OR: Wipf & Stock, 2005 [previously published by Oxford University Press, 1962]).

[249] See CTCR, *Natural Knowledge of God,* 34: "Thus, even while acknowledging the fact of man's natural knowledge of God, the Confessions likewise consistently acknowledge its strict limitations, and even potential dangers if unchecked by the biblical revelation. As previously noted in this regard, the Confessions do not so much stress the lack of natural knowledge about God as they do its falseness. The natural knowledge of God sets forth a distorted picture of Him. It is incapable of showing us the God who justifies and saves from sin."

[250] See Martin H. Franzmann, *Seven Theses on Reformation Hermeneutics* (Commission on Theology and Church Relations of The Lutheran Church—Missouri Synod, 1969), available at http://www.lcms.org/page.aspx?pid=681. Franzmann refers to the Gospel, justification by grace through faith in Christ, as the *res,* or central "subject matter" of Scripture.

[251] See J.A.O. Preus, *It Is Written* (St. Louis: Concordia Publishing House, 1971), 27–28.

a doctrine which is believed solely on the basis of the witness of the Scriptures concerning themselves and not on the basis of empirical verification.[252]

As God's Word, the authority of Scripture is inextricably bound up with the authority of God Himself. This argument has been of critical importance to The Lutheran Church—Missouri Synod throughout its history, but particularly in the 20th century.[253] Thus, in its 1932 "Brief Statement," the LCMS declared:

> the Holy Scriptures differ from all other books in the world in that they are the Word of God ... because the holy men of God who wrote the Scriptures wrote only that which the Holy Ghost communicated to them by inspiration, 2 Tim. 3:16; 2 Pet. 1:21.... Since the Holy Scriptures are the Word of God, it goes without saying that they contain no errors or contradictions, but that they are in all their parts and words the infallible truth, also in those parts which treat of historical, geographical, and other secular matters, John 10:35.[254]

Further, in its 1973 document, "A Statement of Scriptural and Confessional Principles," the Synod underscores that "the opinion that Scripture contains errors is a violation of the [Reformation's] *sola scriptura* [principle], for it rests upon the acceptance of some norm or criterion of truth above the Scriptures."[255] This is a very important argument. The stance of the Reformation is that the Scriptures alone (*sola scriptura*) have final authority: they are the final court of appeal and hence cannot themselves be judged by any higher standard.

It is important to add, however, that this is not a new doctrine or teaching, but is reflected, as indicated, both in the Scriptures themselves and in the writings of Martin Luther and the Lutheran Confessions. Thus, in the *Large Catechism* Luther confesses the complete truthfulness of Scripture, saying "we know that God does not lie [Titus 1:2]. My neighbor and I—in short, all

---

[252] *The Inspiration of Scripture: A Report of the Commission on Theology and Church Relations* (The Lutheran Church—Missouri Synod, 1975), 10.

[253] Controversy within the LCMS and between LCMS theologians and Lutherans from other traditions was acute in the latter half of the 20th century, culminating in the 1970s. This inner-Lutheran debate, however, was reflected within all of Protestantism as well, with a gradual division between so-called mainline Protestants and evangelical Protestants resulting. For an evangelical perspective, see the "Chicago Statement on Biblical Hermeneutics" (1982), available online at http://www.bible-researcher.com/chicago2.html. Article 1 argues that, because Christ himself affirms the complete trustworthiness of Scripture, "one cannot reject the divine authority of Scripture without thereby impugning the authority of Christ."

[254] "Brief Statement of the Doctrinal Position of the Missouri Synod" (Adopted 1932), section 1, "Of the Holy Scriptures," available at: http://www.lcms.org/doctrine/doctrinalposition.

[255] "A Statement of Scriptural and Confessional Principles," The Lutheran Church—Missouri Synod.

people—may deceive and mislead, but God's word cannot deceive."[256] Thus, this conviction is not an outgrowth of the Fundamentalist-Modernist debates of the late 19th and early 20th centuries, nor is it a conservative Lutheran idiosyncrasy. As Ralph Bohlmann has pointed out, historians recognize that

> Belief in the divine inspiration, infallibility, and authority of Holy Scripture was common property of Roman Catholic, Lutheran, Reformed, and other parties involved in the controversies dealt with in the [16th century] Lutheran Confessions . . . .

Indeed, the affirmation of the trustworthiness and authority of Scripture can be traced prior to the Reformation. Bohlmann goes on to quote Arthur Carl Piepkorn.

> If there was one point of universal agreement among all of these [Calvin, Tridentine decrees, pre-Reformation Scholasticism] aside from the nude assertions of the Ecumenical Creeds, it was the authority, the inspiration, and the inerrancy of the Sacred Scriptures.[257]

All of this shows that there can well be and often is a very real barrier that exists between Christian convictions and *scientism*. Conditioned as our culture is by scientism, many people assume that science has the magisterial authority to trump the claims of any other source, including Scripture. In so doing, scientism assumes that Scripture is a merely human document consisting of fallible, revisable claims. Scripture, from the perspective of scientism, is not a revelation from God, but, at most, a book by authors who claim some level of spiritual enlightenment. Therefore it may, of course, contain errors. Yet, as we have shown, this is incompatible with the assertions of Scripture, with long-standing ecumenical Christian tradition, and with the inner logic of Christian revelation—for it directly contradicts the very character of God, who is omniscient, omnipotent and holy. God knows all truth (omniscience, see Ps. 147:5; John 21:17; Heb. 4:13; 1 John 3:20). He can do all that He intends (omnipotence, see Ps. 115:3; Jer. 32:17; Matt. 19:26, Rom. 11:36; Heb. 1:3), including communicating the attributes of His divine nature in the humanity of Jesus (Col. 1:19; Heb. 3:1). Thus He can also communicate truthfully through human language and the words of mortal men.[258] God is holy, He does not deceive us, and indeed, by His very nature, He cannot do so (Num.

---

[256] Large Catechism, IV, 57; KW 464. The German text of the LC seems to emphasize the idea that God will not lie or deceive; the Latin includes the thought that he cannot err. The difference is not profound and the meanings are by no means mutually exclusive. See also the translation in *Concordia: The Lutheran Confessions: A Reader's Edition of the Book of Concord*, trans. W.H.T. Dau and G.F. Bente, trans., (St. Louis: Concordia Publishing House, 2006), 457.

[257] Bohlmann, *Principles of Biblical Interpretation*, 29. The parenthetic brackets and their contents are in the original.

[258] One frequently encounters the idea that what is "written" in Scripture is sure and certain because it is nothing less than God's Word. For example, see 2 Chr. 34:21; Jesus' responses to Satan in his temptation; (Matt. 4:4–11; Luke 19:46; John 15:25; Rom. 3:10; 1 Cor. 14:21; and countless other examples). A similar expression which indicates directly that God himself deigns to

23:19; Ps. 25:8; Is. 6:3; Heb. 6:18). Thus God's word is *infallible* (trustworthy and reliable; incapable of mistake) and *inerrant* (without error) because He is completely *trustworthy* and *without error*.

To be sure, many contemporary theologians have attempted to qualify infallibility and inerrancy by claiming that, while Scripture can be relied on in all "spiritual" matters (such as those concerning our salvation and morality), it need not be inerrant in its claims about "secular" matters, including factual claims about history and science. However, such a claim inherently drives a wedge between God's work as Creator and His works of redemption and spiritual renewal. Orthodox Christianity holds the spiritual and the physical together as two spheres in which God is equally at work. To eliminate one sphere of His work is to eviscerate His work within the other. Essential Christian beliefs have no spiritual significance if they are not grounded in historical fact. Thus, a proper understanding of biblical revelation within history is necessary:

> The Holy Scriptures do not purport to be a textbook of universal history offering an exhaustive account of the history of all nations and peoples from the beginning of time up to the various periods when the Biblical books were written. . . .

> The Bible, however, was written to bear witness to the action of God *in human history* to accomplish the redemption of fallen mankind. If Biblical historical records are unreliable or even false, then God's saving actions in history are called into question too.[259]

One sees this point most dramatically in Paul's straightforward assertion that the truth of the Christian faith depends on the historical fact of the resurrection: "And if Christ has not been raised, your faith is futile and you are still in your sins…. But in fact Christ has been raised from the dead, the firstfruits of those who have fallen asleep" (1 Cor. 15:17, 20). Because an infallible God inspires all of Scripture, we should agree that "since the Holy Scriptures are the Word of God … they are in all their parts and words the infallible truth."[260]

As God's Word, Scripture is necessarily true (John 17:17). God's Word, not science, is the final highest authority for truth even as God always stands in judgment over humankind. But how do we best make use of this "final court of appeal"? Is the Bible the highest standard only in certain ways? How does the Bible become "profitable" (2 Tim. 3:15–17)—particularly with respect to the relationship of science and theology? How are we to read the book of Scripture?

---

use human language are the frequent expressions "Thus says the Lord" (e.g., Ex. 5:1; Is. 44:2) and "declares the Lord" (e.g., Is. 43:10–12; Jer. 31:31–34).

[259] CTCR, *The Inspiration of Scripture*, 11.

[260] "A Statement of Scriptural and Confessional Principles," emphasis added.

3. Reading God's Word— basic principles of interpretation

We have already opened the door to such questions of interpretation earlier in this chapter, by emphasizing that Christians—Lutheran Christians in particular—need always to keep Christ and Scripture together. The Bible is God's Word. In knowing Christ we are led of necessity to value the book of Scripture above the "book" of the world. Only through Scripture's revelation of God in Christ and His justifying and reconciling work can we know Christ authentically and truthfully. The crucial point to emphasize here is that this orientation toward the centrality of the Gospel of Christ and His justifying work for the world is presented by Scripture itself as the way it should be read. Our whole approach to the interpretation of biblical texts is guided by this important orientation. This is the central interpretive principle for the Christian reader of the Bible.[261]

Having identified this central principle, it is helpful to identify additional principles that guide Lutheran Christians in their reading of the Scriptures. Nowhere do the Lutheran Confessions spell out for us a specific list of interpretive principles to which we must all subscribe. Though many Lutheran theologians have provided hermeneutical[262] and exegetical[263] guidelines, none of these lists has, in itself, achieved confessional status among us.[264] The Bible itself does not simply provide a list of interpretive principles by which

---

[261] See Franzmann, *Seven Principles of Reformation Hermeneutics*, who unfolds this further. He emphasizes that the *res* of justification by grace through faith in Christ—Scripture's center—requires that one go back and forth from the words (*verba*) of Scripture to this *res* (summary of its message), "letting Scripture interpret Scripture" and so affirm its central truth (Thesis V, p. 6). This central truth however, does not contradict other truths that are less central, such as the sovereignty of God, the mighty acts of God in Scripture, that he discloses Himself in Scripture, or that the Bible is His verbally inspired and infallible Word (pp. 10–11). Moreover, the Christo-centricity of the Bible leads further, into the use of interpretive tools which reckon with the fact that Christ is revealed through human authors (Thesis VII, pp. 11–12).

[262] *Hermeneutics*, derives from a Greek verb, ἑρμηνεύω (*hermēneuō*), which was used both in the sense of translating a text from a foreign language and in the sense of interpreting any text. In biblical studies, hermeneutics may be simply defined as "principles of interpretation." See James W. Voelz, *What Does This Mean? Principles of Biblical Interpretation in the Post-Modern World*, 2nd ed., rev. (St. Louis: Concordia Publishing House, 2013), 13.

[263] *Exegesis* derives from the Greek verb ἐξηγέομαι (*exēgeomai*), which was used as far back as the fifth century before Christ to indicate the interpretation of a text. Breaking the verb apart into its compounds yields the idea of "leading something out," the idea of this usage being that the interpreter brings out the meaning that is in the text. A simple definition of *exegesis* as a process is "the actual interpretation of the Scriptures." Voelz, 13.

[264] In addition to Franzmann, already noted, see *Aspects of Biblical Hermeneutics: Confessional Principles and Practical Applications*, Concordia Theological Monthly Occasional Papers No. 1 (St. Louis: Concordia Publishing House, 1966); Ralph A. Bohlmann, *Principles of Biblical Interpretation in the Lutheran Confessions* (St. Louis: Concordia Publishing House, 1968). Also helpful in this regard is the Commission on Theology and Church Relations (The Lutheran Church—Missouri Synod), *Gospel and Scripture: The Interrelationship of the Material and Formal Principles in Lutheran Theology* (St. Louis: Concordia Publishing House, 1972).

all its passages are to be understood. There is some risk, then, in providing any list here, since it could easily distract us from our purpose, which is to provide some guidance for the discussion of the real matter at hand here, the relationship between "biblical knowledge" and "scientific knowledge."

The Lutheran Confessions do, however, *model* an approach to Biblical interpretation. As a consequence, when confessional Lutherans have identified principles of interpretation, they always exhibit a significant degree of overlap, even though each has individual characteristics or emphases:[265] The principles below are generally accepted and may be helpful for our discussion here.[266]

1. Pay attention to the context, both literary and historical.

2. Begin with the plain meaning of a text.

3. Scripture interprets Scripture.

4. Interpret Scripture in light of the rule of faith.

5. Interpret Scripture in view of Christ.

6. Distinguish Law and Gospel, sin and grace.

7. Attend to the "then and there" meaning as well as the "here and now" meaning.

These principles are not arranged in priority, but in accordance with the actual task of interpretation. The first two principles are of identical importance for any reader reading any document. One must always *attend to the context* of anything written if one wishes to understand it. Luther once said, "Unless one understands the things under discussion, one cannot make sense of the words."[267] That is true whether one is reading the Bible or the *Wall Street Journal*. For example, the meaning of a particular word, a particular set of letters, will change as it moves through history or from one language to another. Anyone who lives in a multi-lingual or multi-generational setting will have to acknowledge the truth of this observation.

---

[265] Ralph Bohlmann, *Principles of Biblical Interpretation in the Lutheran Confessions*, identifies four central principles: that the Bible is God's Word in its every word; that God the Holy Spirit must enlighten the interpreter to believe the Bible's truths; that the Bible contains both words of condemnation (Law) and forgiveness (Gospel), and the two must be carefully distinguished; and that Christ is the center of all Scripture. Another helpful set of principles is in James Voelz, *What Does This Mean?* (352–358), who lists three: the Christological Principle (Christ's centrality is "the touchstone for the whole" (363); the Coherence Principle (since God is author of all Scripture, it has a unified message), and the Integrity Principle (each individual passage must be allowed to retain its particular understanding and truth).

[266] These principles are adapted from the list provided by Lane A. Burgland, *How to Read the Bible with Understanding*, 2d ed. (St. Louis: Concordia Publishing House, 2015 [forthcoming]).

[267] Franzmann, *Seven Theses*, 2.

It is sadly obvious that the Bible can be misused and that quotations from it can be used in twisted and corrupt ways. The Bible itself recognizes this. The apostle Peter warns about the misuse of Paul's epistles and of other Scriptures: "There are some things in them that are hard to understand, which the ignorant and unstable twist to their own destruction, as they do the other Scriptures" (2 Pet. 3:16). So it is that the Bible is to be read in the recognition of the significance that the contexts of its particular books and segments have for its meaning. The coming of Christ marks the great difference in the context of the Old Testament in comparison to the New. Each of the Gospels has its own contextual traits. Although both James and Paul write epistles, each writes from within a different context, and, indeed, each of Paul's epistles (and every other biblical book) must be considered within its own context.

Secondly, every document must be taken, first, at face value (*accepting Scripture's plain meaning*).[268] That is, one reads before he reacts to what he reads. This is all the more important, however, for one who reads Scripture. We pass judgment, of necessity, on the writings of other people, recognizing that they are not infallible. We cannot, however, pass judgment on God's Word, for God judges us. Consider a woman who reads in a newspaper about a miraculous claim. She understands exactly what is claimed, because the meaning is plain, but she may also doubt that it is true because such miraculous events are, by their very definition, uncommon. The presupposition that nature is all that exists (hence, that natural laws are absolute) leads many to treat Scripture in an identical manner. It leads people to doubt or read an allegorical or personal "existential" meaning into a biblical text that makes a miraculous claim, and thus simply to ignore the claim itself. For one who receives the Scriptures as God's Word, however, unless the biblical text itself warrants such an alternative reading, this cannot constitute sound exegesis. That such a reading finds support in a popular (or academically fashionable) worldview external to the text is irrelevant: a sound reading must be grounded in *what the text actually says*. The faithful reader of Scripture takes the plain meaning—of a healing by Jesus, for example—and accepts its truth without quibbles, for he or she knows Jesus to be Lord of heaven and earth.

In order for the church to build doctrines confidently on the statements of Scripture, its focus must be on their primary and intended meaning rather than (like medieval scholastics or modern critics) on speculation about possible allegorical or mythological readings. This does not ignore the fact that figures of speech clearly do occur in Scripture. For example, mountains metaphorically sing for joy (e.g., Ps. 98:8; Is. 42:11; 44:23; 49:13). God the Father has a "right hand," but not one made of flesh and bone (e.g., Ex. 15:6; Ps. 110:1; 118:15; Luke 22:69; Rom. 8:34). Taking account of the literary genre of a text, on the basis of the internal evidence supplied by Scripture itself, is crucial

---

[268] The plain meaning of the text includes the assumption that the text is using language in a way that is consistent with its use at the time of the composition of the text itself. See the discussion of principle 7 below.

here. The Psalms and other biblical poems, for example (as one might expect), are filled with figures of speech. But the reports of Jesus' miracles (e.g., his miracles of healing in Luke 5:12–13; 5:24–25; 6:10; 7:10; 7:14–15) provide no internal basis for the assumption that they are describing anything other than actual events in a straightforward way. Any claim that these reports were merely metaphorical or were parables rather than descriptions of events would seem to depend on the exegete's prior assumption that miracles cannot really happen. It is not grounded in the content or structure of the texts, which naturally read as historical narrative. A speculative approach that privileges an allegorical reading of Scripture makes it easy to dismiss passages of Scripture that appear to create scientific, cultural or personal difficulties by simply declaring them to have an obscure meaning. In this way many have dismissed, for example, the opening verses of Genesis as mythical or allegorical, because they find them to be in conflict with a naturalistic evolutionary account of the origin of life and of its diversity.

The third principle, that *Scripture interprets Scripture*, also has a connection to the exegesis of other books and documents. When a novel introduces a character, it builds on that same characterization throughout. If a science text defines a term, the reader will then be able to understand that term when it is used elsewhere in the same text without definition. Similarly, the Bible tells of God, providing a characterization that is developed in various ways—notably as both one in being (Deut. 6:4), yet also, mysteriously, three in persons (Matt. 28:19). If Scripture consistently portrays God as Creator of heaven and earth (Neh. 9:6; Is. 45:12; Jon. 1:9), from nothing (Rom. 4:17; Heb. 11:3), merely by speaking (Ps. 33:6; 2 Pet. 3:5), and in the span of six days (Ex. 31:17; Heb. 4:4), then that, indeed, is how we are to understand the creation of the world. If Scripture consistently portrays God as forming man from the dust (Gen. 3:19; 1 Cor. 15:47–49), forming the woman subsequently from man's rib (1 Cor. 11:8; 1 Tim. 2:13), and creating both in His divine image (Gen. 9:6; Col. 3:10), then that is how we are to understand the origin of humanity.

To *interpret Scripture in light of the rule of faith* (principle 4) is unique to scriptural interpretation. It is, together with the fifth, sixth, and seventh principles, directly connected to what we have emphasized earlier about the role that knowing Christ and His justifying work—that is, the Gospel—plays in one's approach to Scripture. Martin Franzmann's work, cited above, beautifully lays out the importance of reading Scripture in light of the "rule of faith" (his preferred term is *res*, that is, its central message).[269] He shows how throughout the Bible's historical books (Genesis to Esther), the great

---

[269] Franzmann's concern is with what may be called the material principle of theology. The term indicates the central teaching of Christian faith, the Gospel. The material principle is coupled with the "formal principle," that is, Scripture—the form by which the Gospel message is given to us. This distinction and the importance of retaining these principles rightly is discussed at length in the CTCR's report, *Gospel and Scripture: The Interrelationship of the Material and Formal Principles in Lutheran Theology* (1972).

"melody line" (another expression akin to the rule of faith) is God's grace despite the rebellion, sin, failures, and brokenness of humanity in general and Israel in particular.[270] The prophets make this "radical Gospel" all the more plain, portraying a corrupt and crushed nation nonetheless finding promised redemption in Israel's God.[271] And—of particular importance to this report—even as the Bible's "Wisdom Literature" (Job to Song of Songs) is emphatic in the value it gives to human wisdom and understanding (and we might add, science), it nonetheless reminds us that no such accomplishments "can avail," ultimately, and "the victory belongs to the Lord" and to Him alone.[272] Under this same principle, the rule of faith, we would also mention the role the ecumenical Creeds play as shorthand forms of the central biblical truth of who the one God is—Father, Son, and Holy Spirit—and what He has done in creating the world, redeeming it from sin and death, and purifying and renewing His people. It is in Christ, then, that the New Testament fulfills all of this utterly gracious, justifying, redeeming work of God for Israel and the nations.[273]

From this, both the fifth principle (*interpretation in view of Christ*) and the sixth (*distinguish Law and Gospel, sin and grace*) from Burgland's list are immediately obvious. We have amply addressed the fifth principle above. As we have noted, Christ stands at the center, for "he is before all things, and in him all things hold together" (Col. 1:17)—including, of course, the Scriptures and their message. All sound exegesis must begin and ever return to Christ Jesus, the revelation of God (Matt. 11:27).

Moreover, regarding the sixth principle, it is certain that only in Christ does humanity's failure to keep God's law, and all human sin and rebellion, find an answer in the Gospel—the Good News of Christ's gracious, redeeming death and resurrection. To read Scripture with careful distinction between Law and Gospel, sin and grace, is to recognize that Jesus stands at the center of Scripture because of His saving work. It is also to recognize that the means by which the Holy Spirit does His renewing and sanctifying work is the Word of God itself, which first makes plain human sin and God's righteous condemnation and threatened punishment (Law), but then so beautifully also declares us righteous because of the life, suffering, death, and resurrection of Jesus Christ, His Son, our Lord (Gospel). Bohlmann has summarized this principle, reminding us that a person who has been justified by grace through faith in Christ "knows that in Holy Scripture God speaks a condemnatory word (Law) and a forgiving word (Gospel), the former for the sake of the latter."[274] The Apology of the Augsburg Confession explains:

---

[270] Franzmann, *Seven Theses*, 6–7.

[271] Ibid., 7–8.

[272] Ibid., 8, quoting Prov. 21:30–31.

[273] Ibid., 9–10.

[274] Bohlmann, *Principles of Biblical Interpretation*, 65.

For these are the two chief works of God in human beings, to terrify and to justify the terrified or make them alive. The entire Scripture is divided into these two works. One part is the law, which reveals, denounces, and condemns sin. The second part is the gospel, that is, the promise of grace given in Christ.[275]

This twin message is part and parcel of the central truth of Scripture—it is "constantly repeated" in a variety of ways throughout Scripture in its entirety.[276]

The seventh principle, *attending to the meaning "then and there" and also the meaning "here and now,"* is a caution against superficial readings of Scripture. One might assume from the first few principles, especially the second, that the Bible is always easy to understand. But that would be to ignore the fact that the Bible was written millennia ago in a world far different from our own. Its truths, intended for the whole of humanity, were revealed within particular human circumstances, in specific times and places. So ordinary Bible readers can and should give thanks that God has called for His Church to set aside servants—pastors and teachers in particular—who are "able to teach" (1 Tim. 3:2; 2 Tim. 2:2, 24) because they have studied God's Word deeply, learning the languages of its original authors and the customs, practices, and idiosyncrasies of that particular world from long ago. It is by carefully understanding the "then and there" language, setting, and meaning that we are able best to speak of the "here and now" meaning of the Bible. In attending to this principle the Bible reader will understand, to use a simple example, that while the commandments forbid coveting our neighbor's "male servant, or his female servant, or his ox, or his donkey," they by no means exempt our coveting of status, cars, and so forth.[277]

4. Biblical Exegesis and Modern Science

For our purposes here, the important question is to understand how proper biblical exegesis relates with the discoveries, models and theories of science. Has the Bible been discredited because it sometimes appears to be in conflict with knowledge gleaned from science?

As we have seen in the preceding sections, God does not reveal Himself in some eternal language of heaven, which doubtless we, as finite, fallen

---

[275] Ap XII, 53.

[276] Ibid.

[277] Exodus 20:17. This is not the place to investigate fully the prerequisite knowledge and skill of the Biblical reader. Knowledge of language and linguistics, of history and culture, of theology and rhetoric, all contribute to the successful carrying out of the exegetical task. What is important to mention here is that this training and formation does not happen in isolation from other readers. Readers are formed by communities that have themselves already assumed the role of reader and interpreter of the text in question. A helpful discussion of this is found in Voelz, 220–221.

creatures, could not understand. Rather, He reveals Himself through human language that is shaped by the world as it appears to human beings. This is very clearly illustrated by Jesus' frequent assertion that "The kingdom of heaven is like ..." (for example, in Matt. 13). The Scriptures generally describe the world according to what philosopher Wilfrid Sellars (1912–1989) called its "manifest image"[278]—the way it *appears* to us using our five senses and according to our given, common-sense reactions to it. Even when it recounts the marvelous and transcendent (such as in reports of miracles and the events of visionary and apocalyptic literature) it provides images that are sense perceptible. Even as God communicated most profoundly to human beings by becoming man in the person of Jesus Christ, so also He inspired fallible human beings to communicate infallibly His truth as it was spoken by prophets and apostles and preserved infallibly in the inerrant Scriptures.

A consequence of God's communication to humans by way of the manifest image is that scriptural texts of apparent scientific import should not be reinterpreted in light of current, highly specialized, scientific theories, but should be taken as accurate reports of the way things appear to sensory human beings. Thus in the famous example of Joshua 10:12–13 (discussed at length in chapter 1), we should limit our interpretation of the text to the claim that, from an earthbound perspective, the sun *appeared* to stand still. This is doubtless compatible with a variety of scientific interpretations,[279] but none of these can claim to be derived from text itself. This is because the Holy Spirit inspired the writers to use human words whose original meanings had not been shaped by these scientific theories. For scientifically literate people today, talk of a stationary sun has been shaped by these theoretical advances, but it would be an anachronistic equivocation to read our meaning back into the ancient writings themselves. This is why inerrancy is not "negated by Biblical phenomena such as a lack of modern technical precision," or by "observational descriptions of nature," or, as another example, by the use of "round numbers."[280] Carl Henry nicely explains this point:

> Inerrancy does not imply that modern technological precision in reporting statistics and measurements, that conformity to modern historiographic method in reporting genealogies and other historical data, or that modern scientific method in reporting cosmological matters, can be expected from the biblical writers .... We have no right to impose upon the biblical

---

[278] Wilfrid Sellars, "Philosophy and the Scientific Image of Man," in ed. Robert Colodny, *Frontiers of Science and Philosophy* (Pittsburgh: University of Pittsburgh Press, 1962): 35–78.

[279] For some of the possibilities here, see Robert Dick Wilson's "Understanding 'The Sun Stood Still'," in ed. Walter Kaiser, *Classical Evangelical Essays in Old Testament Interpretation* (Grand Rapids: Baker Book House, 1972), 61–65. A controversial feature of this essay's orientation is that the author seems very concerned to avoid a miraculous interpretation of Joshua 10.

[280] "Chicago Statement on Biblical Inerrancy" Article XIII. Available at: http://www.bible-researcher.com/chicago1.html.

writers methods of classifying information that are specifically oriented to the scientific interests of our time, or to require their use of scientifically technical language, or to demand the computerized precision cherished by a technological civilization.[281]

This should warn us also against perhaps overly zealous scientifically minded apologetic arguments that claim to have discovered that the Scriptures anticipated or give direct insight into such things as relativity theory, quantum mechanics, or dark matter. The text is indeed inspired, but what was inspired were human words whose meanings are to be found in their normal usage at the time the original autographs were written—and that usage was not shaped by any of these scientific theories.

We would do well also to examine several assumptions which may lead to false or inaccurate conclusions regarding the claims of Scripture and of science. Certain questions may be beneficial when biblical statements and scientific conclusions seem incompatible.

Are we talking about the same thing?

In order for two statements to conflict, they must be speaking about the same subject, and one statement must affirm what the other denies about that subject. If one person says "apples are green or red," and another says "oranges are orange," the claims do not conflict because they have a different subject matter. Likewise, there is no conflict if someone says "oranges are orange" and another says "oranges contain Vitamin C," because neither person denies what the other person affirms. However, if one person claims that oranges contain Vitamin C and the other person claims that oranges do not contain Vitamin C, then there is a conflict. Conflict requires that there are two assertions about the same subject (oranges), that both use terms with the *same meaning* ("oranges," "contain," "Vitamin C") to describe it, and that these terms are used both to affirm and deny the very same claim about the subject.[282]

If both parties are competent users of the same language and employ standard contemporary usage, the meaning of terms is usually straightforward.[283] Matters are not so easy when comparing contemporary scientific

---

[281] Carl F. Henry, *God, Revelation and Authority*, vol. 4, *God Who Speaks and Shows* (Waco, TX: Word, 1979), 201.

[282] This principle is specifically applied to the alleged discrepancies regarding the Gospels' accounts of the healing of the blind at Jericho and the accounts of Matthew and Luke in Acts of the death of Judas in William Arndt, *Bible Difficulties & Seeming Contradictions*, rev. ed. (St. Louis: Concordia, 1987), 178–179, 184.

[283] One should not assume, of course—even for competent users of the same language, that meanings are always straightforward, since individuals often use the same term with differing emphases or nuances. Logicians call attention to *the fallacy of equivocation*, where the same term is used with two (or more) different meanings. For example, if one says a car is hot, another might misunderstand this to mean the car was stolen when the intended meaning was that car had a high temperature.

claims to ancient biblical texts. Even in those cases when, according to *our* established usage, a biblical text seems to comment on a scientific matter, we must remember that the original, intended meaning of the biblical text generally reflects *the usage of language "then and there"*[284] and that usage was not shaped by the claims, procedures, theories and findings of modern science. Without this caution, there is a very serious danger of anachronism, which will read the contemporary meanings of words within science back into an ancient text. For example, when Genesis speaks of God creating plants, trees, and land creatures according to their *kind*, it cannot automatically be assumed that "kind" lines up neatly with the taxonomical categories recognized by modern biology. "God did not classify animals thousands of years ago according to our modern classification system."[285]

Similarly, it is not easy to determine the identity of the marine animal that swallowed Jonah (Jon. 1:17; Matt. 12:40), as the words used in the original languages (*dag gadol*, "fish" in Hebrew; *ketos*, "sea monster" in Greek) are simply generic terms and are not specific.[286] While observations of the flora, fauna, archeology, hydrology, psychology, and sociology of a people may provide insights that help to clarify what these texts are saying, the exegete must resist reading the contemporary categories of modern scientific taxonomy back into the scriptural text, but should instead try to recognize the actual conceptual categories in use at the time of the text's composition.

Who is the audience?

With reference to the audience of Scripture, there is the matter of reconciling the particular with the universal. Scripture reflects the seeming paradox that there is both an original audience of a text and also a universal audience, since God's Word has a catholic or universal application for all humanity.[287] Despite the historical particularities of its formulations, all of God's Word is intended for all people at all times. Its purpose is eternal or eschatological, not temporal, so its direction is from the particularities of this world to the world God has promised and has already inaugurated in Christ Jesus.

---

[284] See principle 7, pp. 107–111. One may also note, however, that God in His omniscience may mean more than the inspired human author himself understood. This is sometimes referred to as a *sensus plenior*. So, for example, our Lord says all of the Old Testament testifies of Him (Luke 24:44-47), even though that testimony is frequently indirect, not direct.

[285] See Eric Lyons, "Was Jonah Swallowed by a Fish or a Whale?" available at: http://www.apologeticspress.org/APContent.aspx?category=6&article=2830.

[286] See *A Greek-English Lexicon of the New Testament and other Early Christian Literature*. 3rd ed., Frederick William Danker, ed. (Chicago and London: The University of Chicago Press, 2000): 544; and Ludwig Koehler and Walter Baumgartner, *The Hebrew and Aramaic Lexicon of the Old Testament*. 5 vols. (Leiden: Brill, 1994), 1: 213. For a more general response to alleged biological errors in the Bible, see Eric Lyons, "Did the Bible Writers Commit Biological Blunders," available at: http://www.apologeticspress.org/apPubPage.aspx?pub=1&issue=615&article=736.

[287] This also is a direct application of principle 7, p. 111 above. In addition, it is an aspect of principles 1 and 2, pp. 108–109. The term catholicity is used here with reference to the universal dimension of all Christian truth and thus the church herself and the Scriptures.

Since the original texts of Scripture are in Hebrew, Aramaic, and Greek, they must be studied in light of their original language and setting.[288] Our Lord Jesus lived within a particular geographic locale, ate the foods of that particular region, spoke the language of that place, wore the garments of that time, and generally experienced the total panoply of cultural expressions of that day. Nevertheless, His life and the truths He spoke are for all time. This becomes explicit in His command to preach His Gospel to all nations (Matt. 28:19–20). It is all the more apparent because of the remarkable fact that His life and words were preserved not in the language He spoke (Aramaic) nor in the language of the Hebrew Scriptures that He read and fulfilled, but in the language of the surrounding first century world—Greek. The record of the profoundly particular life, death, resurrection, and teachings of this first century Jew has thus, from the beginning, been translated into one language after another. As it is heard in their own tongue by one more far-off people after another, faith arises (Rom. 10:17) in the one Lord Jesus and His Gospel— in the one God of all people, Father, Son, and Holy Spirit.[289]

This also means that every hearing of Scripture requires attention to cultural details that may be "foreign." For example, the parable of the great banquet (Luke 14:12–24) includes details that are alien to an American today—reclining at a table, yokes of oxen—yet it shows us eternal truths about fallen mankind and the love and grace of God. It shows us that all fallen people are blind, lame beggars, weak and handicapped with no power to save themselves, and it shows that God's saving grace is offered to all. Science works in a different direction. Its purpose is temporal, not eternal. Science explores how this world works. Its goals are ultimately practical in terms of this world. To the extent that science discovers enduring principles or truths, it seeks thereby to apply them to present problems and difficulties, not eternal ones.

On rare occasions, the particularity and even peculiarity of Scripture's language and imagery may mean we cannot be sure of some specific details about a text. An example is the meaning of the "star of Bethlehem." Matthew 2:1–9 tells us of a "star in the East" that guides the wise men to the birthplace of Christ, and scholars have puzzled over just what this "star" refers to. Most important is that we cannot assume that "star" means what it does in modern astronomical theory, which carefully distinguishes between planets, comets and stars. The Greek word for "star" used in Matthew is *aster*." This

---

[288] One corollary principle of biblical inspiration is that the original autographs of Scripture were inspired in their particular languages (Hebrew, Aramaic and Greek) with a meaning determined by the usage of words in their world. Thus it is important not only to attempt to reconstruct the original text from the comparison of extant manuscripts, but also to labor to understand what that text originally meant in the minds of its authors and intended recipients.

[289] For a profound and provocative consideration of the importance of the translation of the Scriptures, see Lamin Sanneh, *Translating the Message: The Missionary Impact on Culture* (Maryknoll, NY: Orbis Books, 1989).

can signify any luminous body, so it does not distinguish between planets, comets, and what we today call stars. Thus it is not surprising that modern commentators have proposed theories along each of these lines (and more besides).[290] In favor of the planetary theory is that there was a conjunction of Jupiter, Saturn, and Mars in 6 BC, but it is doubtful it would have looked like a single heavenly body, if indeed it was fully visible at all.[291] There is some plausibility in the ideas of a comet or even of a nova which occurs when a star has a sudden increase in its luminosity because of an internal explosion.[292] Yet the text does not tell us whether the "star" was a natural phenomenon (it certainly could have been, since God knows from eternity when some unusual natural phenomenon will occur, and can certainly use it as a sign) or a special miracle. Some think clues in the text suggest the latter option, for how can an ordinary star go before people and rest at a particular location? But others point out that this may just refer to the apparent motion of the star, since "as people travel, the stars do seem to move with them or before them, stopping when they stop."[293] The point of the emphasis here is that inerrancy does not imply that we always *know* what every detail of the original text means, it only implies that the original meaning expresses truth. What we can say with confidence is that the mysterious star is an extraordinary illustration of the fact that God desires all to know His Son as Lord and King—including those from faraway and once hostile lands (Eph. 2:17; 1 Tim. 2:4).

Are we speaking in similar ways?

There are also subtle matters of genre identification. The genre of a text concerns the particular class of literature that text belongs to by virtue of its form, content, style, and technique. A variety of genres is employed in Scripture, such as historical narrative, regulations and laws, prophecies, psalms, poetry, and so forth. If faulty exegesis is to be avoided, identification of the genre of the text must be grounded in the text itself. Poetic or metaphorical expressions may then be identified as such without implying a literal meaning (for example, in Psalm 104:3 the Lord is said to make the clouds His chariot). Thus, parallels with similar texts and literary conventions of the time can be illuminating; however, they are not conclusive as to a biblical text's meaning.[294] Moreover, judgment about the genre of a biblical text can-

---

[290] See chapter 7 of Paul Maier's *In the Fullness of Time: A Historian Looks at Christmas, Easter, and the Early Church* (Grand Rapids: Kregel Publications, 1991).

[291] Ibid., 55.

[292] Ibid., 58.

[293] Ibid., 59–60.

[294] This principle does not deny that parallel texts outside of Scripture can help to illuminate the genre of a biblical text. For example, many scholars have argued persuasively that the Mosaic covenant as expressed in Exodus and Deuteronomy has many of the same structural elements as does a typical Suzerain-Vassal treaty of the ancient near east such as those employed by the Hittites. The Biblical texts follow a structure similar to the suzerainty treaties, with a preamble, historical prologue, list of stipulations, and an associated list of blessings for obedi-

not be based on whether the text seems plausible in light of modern scientific claims. [295] Thus, one cannot suppose that the creation of the world by the spoken Word of God is a poetic metaphor without any literal basis because it seems to conflict with a modern scientific claim about the origins of the earth. This is an irresponsible interpretation because it does not establish the genre of the text on the basis of the form, content, style, and technique of the text itself, but rather suggests a convenient literary escape route from an apparent scientific embarrassment.

When Psalm 98:8 expresses this response—"Let the rivers clap their hands; let the hills sing for joy together"—no one supposes this is a scientific prediction of some rather unusual behavior by rivers and hills. Yet it should be noticed that the text itself makes it abundantly clear that this is a praise song (v. 1, 5, 6). There are other clues as well, such as Hebrew parallelisms within Psalm 98 and within the surrounding context of similar psalms, such as musical directions which indicate that this is a species of poetry (a song of praise) in which metaphor and figures of speech are to be expected. On the other hand, it would be far different to claim that Jesus' miracles of healing are only metaphorical, especially when Jesus himself instructs John the Baptist's disciples to tell John about the miracles that they "hear and see" (Matt. 11: 4). What they heard about and saw with their own eyes were healings of the blind, the lame, the diseased, and the deaf, not inspiring metaphors for something else. There is nothing in the texts that report these miracles to suggest that they are metaphorical or mythological, so any suggestion along those lines derives primarily from assumptions external to the text (e.g., naturalism).

A well-known illustration of erroneous genre identification is the attempt to show that Genesis 1 is a mythological text, because of its superficial resemblance to the ancient Babylonian creation myth, *Enuma Elish*.[296] Close study of the texts in parallel reveals major differences.[297] For example, *Enuma*

---

ence and curses for breach of covenant. That discovery can help us to see that God's covenant with his people takes the form of a recognized legal agreement and serves both religious and civil purposes. However, it does not follow from such formal similarities that the content of the biblical covenant is simply borrowed or merely a human political document that adapts existing legislation. The *kind* of agreement God is making with His people—a matter that depends in part on determining the genre of the text (e.g., what sort of contract or treaty is it, and what are its terms?)—can be discerned only by a close reading of its own claims. That meaning should make sense in light of the ancient near east context, but we should not presume it is merely borrowed. Recognition of the merits of the text itself reveals that the Mosaic covenant is quite unique in its content.

[295] See principles 1 and 2, p. 107–109.

[296] The full text of the *Enuma Elish* is available here: http://www.sacred-texts.com/ane/stc/ index.htm. See also the one-page summary chart in John H. Walton, *Chronological and Background Charts of the Old Testament* (Grand Rapids: Zondervan, 1978, 1994), 80.

[297] An excellent summary of the superficial similarities and major underlying differences is provided by Jared Wellman, "Does the Genesis creation account come from the Babylonian Enuma Elish?" available at: http://carm.org/genesis-creation-enuma-elish.

Elish is polytheistic, not monotheistic; the gods themselves seem subject to powers of nature (indeed they seem to be part of nature, and are mortal); and it is not an account of the creation of the entire universe from nothing: the patron deity Marduk creates the heavens and the earth by dividing the body of Tiamat, another god he has slain (Tablet 4), and Ea fashions human beings from the blood of Kingu (Tablet 6). It is a fallacy of faulty analogy to argue that because two texts have some superficial similarities and one text belongs to a particular genre, that therefore the other text shares that genre. By this argument, realistic novels could be declared non-fiction and the moving account of an actual trial could be declared fiction. Even if it is true that some images or ideas are common to the *Enuma Elish* and Genesis, the fact remains that Genesis makes unique claims about the Creator and the creation—most notably that Yahweh is the one true God, that He transcends his creation (and is not part of it or subject to it), and that He alone brings all else into being.

By whose authority are we speaking?

In each of the foregoing examples there is an improper reading of the biblical text, resulting in something other than its intended meaning. However, there is also a fundamentally different understanding of authority, as we indicated in section 2. Does final authority lie with the Word of God or the claims of science? This challenge to biblical authority is no surprise because, with the rise of autonomous reason, all forms of authority have been challenged. As Carl Henry said several decades ago,

> Anyone who thinks that this problem specially or exclusively embarrasses Bible believers has not listened to the wild winds of defiance now sweeping over much of modern life. Respect for authority is being challenged on almost every front and in almost every form.[298]

A contemporary example of this is the undermining of the Bible's moral authority. In recent years some theologians have claimed that Romans 1:26–27 does not really speak against sexual activity between persons of the same sex, but is rather focused on more specific abuses such as temple prostitution or pedophilia—that this is what the writers actually had in mind.[299] What drives this argument, however, is the presupposition of contemporary social science that homosexuality is one among many natural orientations and that therefore this *cannot* be what Paul is opposing. The trouble is that this conclusion cannot be derived from the words of the text: these words neither mention nor suggest temple prostitution, pedophilia, or any other such qualifications. Sound exegesis requires that we draw the meaning out of the words actually in the text. While contextual studies can help us to understand the meaning of

---

[298] Carl F. Henry, *God, Revelation and Authority*, vol. 4., 7–8.

[299] For an example of this and a response to it within Lutheranism see the CTCR report, *Response to Human Sexuality: Gift and Trust*, online at http://lcms.org/Document.fdoc?src=lcm&id=1820.

those words, they cannot add, delete, or modify the words themselves or their meaning. If they could, Scripture would simply become "a wax nose to be pulled to and fro"[300] and adapted to say whatever we would prefer it to mean. What was reasonable to the autonomous individual, rather than the text itself, would determine the text's "meaning" and Scripture's divine Author and His authority would be ignored.

On matters of scientific import, then, the implication is that we should not simply read contemporary science into the original text. For example, in describing the creation of the world, there is no reason to think that, even under inspiration, Moses had in mind some modern cosmological theory that modern scientists regard as plausible. Nothing in the text suggests that Moses was an early advocate of modern string theory or speculated about multiple universes! At the same time, one should be careful to note that the scriptural text may not *clearly and directly rule out all such theories*. On the one hand, it is possible that the text is simply silent on some matters as they were simply not on the radar (to use an anachronistic metaphor!) when the text was written. On the other hand, the plain sense of Genesis 1:1 ("In the beginning, God created the heavens and the earth") and Matthew 24:35 ("Heaven and earth will pass away, but my words will not pass away") is surely incompatible with the view held in common by Ancient Greek philosophers[301] and "steady state" cosmologists (like Sir James Jeans in the 1920s[302]) that the existence of matter has neither a beginning nor an end.

Areas of uncertainty: humility in interpretation and confidence in Christ

Of course, while we rightly confess the conviction that Scripture is infallible, we also recognize that its interpreters are not. So it may happen that further study makes orthodox interpreters question assumptions or conclusions about a biblical text and its relationship to scientific knowledge. The case of Copernicus is an example. Nevertheless, faithful scholars should be on guard against fundamental re-readings of texts (for example, reading the creation accounts of Genesis 1 and 2 as mere mythology), and scientifically minded people may have to simply accept that when God's Word meets the works of human science, we cannot always produce a tidy rapprochement.

---

[300] This was Luther's charge against some of the theologians of Rome in his day. See Luther's "The Papacy at Rome: An Answer to the Celebrated Romanist at Leipzig," (1520). AE 39:81.

[301] Plato and Aristotle both took for granted that matter had always been here, and assumed that what required explanation was not the existence of matter (a brute fact) but its structure or form. Thus in Plato's *Timaeus*, matter is shaped into the likeness of the eternal forms, and in Aristotelian metaphysics, formal causes explained their structure.

[302] The steady state theory hypothesizes that there is a continuous creation of new matter, so that the universe has no origin or termination. This theory is widely rejected because of the overwhelming evidence that the universe came into existence a finite time ago.

As we have shown, the Bible cannot be isolated from science—the two cannot simply be segregated from one another. Contrary to NOMA's central tenet, biblical truths *do overlap* with scientific ones. It is important to emphasize, however, that the overlap is not comprehensive. The Bible does not speak directly to many different topics and situations that science addresses. Scripture is not an encyclopedia of all human knowledge, but it is the inspired record of God's particular work in history—especially the incarnation and saving work of His Son. The salvific purpose of Scripture is central, not microbiology or agronomy or physics or other human scientific disciplines. Scripture does not contain comprehensive truths about such sciences and it is a misuse of Scripture to think the Bible will give us clarity about scientific questions that it does not answer or even intend to address.

Scripture is very clear, first and foremost, about its central and primary truth: Christ and His saving work. Theologians often refer to the clarity of Scripture as its "perspicuity." Francis Pieper asserts: "According to Scripture, the perspicuity of Scripture consists in this, that it presents, in language that can be understood by all, whatever men must know to be saved."[303] The Gospel, of course, is not the only truth that Scripture clearly teaches. Pieper goes on to say that "Scripture is perfectly clear and is in regard to doctrine and life 'a lamp unto our feet and a light unto our path.'"[304] Thus, every aspect of Christian teaching ("doctrine and life") is made clear in Scripture. Reminding us of the consistency of this idea and its importance in Lutheran theology (as is evident in its Confessions) the CTCR report on *Gospel and Scripture* states:

> The whole body of Lutheran doctrine is always represented as "taken from the Word of God and solidly and well grounded therein" (FC SD Summary, 5) "supported with clear and irrefutable testimonies from the Holy Scriptures" (*ibid.*, 6), and based "on the witness of the unalterable truth of the divine Word" (Preface to *The Book of Concord*, p. 5).[305]

The Bible makes perfectly clear that God "desires all people to be saved and to come to the knowledge of the truth" (1 Tim. 2:4). Furthermore, we can be confident that an omnipotent, omniscient, and holy God will be clear in His revelation of all that we must know to be saved and to live according to God's good and gracious will. Indeed, God Himself tells us that His Word cannot fail:

> For as the rain and the snow come down from heaven
>   and do not return there but water the earth,
>   making it bring forth and sprout,

---

[303] *Christian Dogmatics,* vol. 1 (St. Louis: Concordia Publishing House, 1950), 320. Pieper has a lengthy section on this doctrine on 319–329.

[304] Ibid., 324. See also Bohlmann, *Principles of Biblical Interpretation,* 53–63.

[305] *Gospel and Scripture,* 9.

giving seed to the sower and bread to the eater,
so shall my word be that goes out from my mouth;
it shall not return to me empty,
but it shall accomplish that which I purpose,
and shall succeed in the thing for which I sent it. (Is. 55:10–11)

And toward the end of John's Gospel, we are clearly told its primary purpose:

Now Jesus did many other signs in the presence of the disciples, which are not written in this book; but these are written so that you may believe that Jesus is the Christ, the Son of God, and that by believing you may have life in his name. (John 20:30–31)

As Christians, we can know with certainty that God has revealed His plan of salvation to us, and more generally, that even if we struggle with some difficult passages here and there, we can be confident that "All Scripture is breathed out by God and profitable for teaching, for reproof, for correction, and for training in righteousness, that the man of God may be complete, equipped for every good work" (2 Tim. 3:16–17). This passage tells us that the Scriptures are sufficiently clear for effective instruction *in all areas of the Christian life and teaching*. If this were not so, the Church would be unable to carry out the Great Commission of making "disciples of all nations" and "teaching them to observe *all*" that Jesus commanded (Matt. 28:19–20, emphasis added).

The Bible is clear about those doctrines essential to salvation and Christian living. This means that if there is a text that expresses a doctrinal truth in a way that is less than clear to us, we can be sure that it is also expressed more clearly in some other passage of Scripture. And since Scripture interprets Scripture, we can and should consult these clearer passages to aid in illuminating the meaning of those that are less clear.

It must again be stressed that clarity in "doctrine and life" or "salvation and Christian living" should not be misunderstood as meaning that the Bible clearly teaches *only* spiritual or moral truths. Scripture clearly reveals truths about God's world and the history of His saving work that are "historical" and "scientific" even when they tell about what God did in extraordinary and miraculous ways.[306] In His Word the Triune God reveals Himself to be a God who is fully involved with creation—both in its initial perfection and in its fallen present state. His work of redemption involves His being flesh and blood and His mysterious work of spiritual renewal involves vocal chords, sound waves, and dirty feet that carry a preacher from one place to the next

---

[306] The terms "historical" and "scientific" are employed here to indicate factuality. Thus, an event, such as the Exodus from Egypt, must be understood as historically factual because Scripture speaks clearly about its occurrence. So also, an event, such as the raising of Lazarus must be understood as factual in that a scientifically minded physician could have observed and documented first the fact of Lazarus's death and then of his return to life.

(Rom. 10:14–15). In his discussion of the principle of scriptural clarity in the Lutheran confessions, Ralph Bohlmann writes:

> We note that all articles of faith, the sacraments, and Old Testament sacrifices are included within the compass of Biblical clarity. Moreover, the clarity of Scripture is clearly related to Biblical language. It is therefore not in keeping with the confessional understanding of the clarity of Scripture to limit it primarily to those passages "which display the teaching of justification by grace through faith in all its force and glory."[307]

We can also be certain that the power of Scripture is not limited by what we find easy to understand. We know that the efficacy of Baptism comes from God's Word, even though the infant does not understand that Word. The power of the Word does not depend on our ability to respond, as if the Word was inert and our minds were the determining factor. Rather, the Word of God is alive and active (Heb. 4:12). It was through the Word of God that the universe was created (Ps. 33:6; Heb. 11:3), and it is through the Word that those dead in sin are brought to new life in Christ (1 Pet. 1:23). It is also through the Word that the Holy Spirit seeks to bring us to the inner clarity of faith that accepts such clear truths even when our minds cannot fully comprehend them.[308]

Still, there are areas of uncertainty. God has not revealed everything to us in His Word (Eccl. 3:11; 1 Cor. 13:9–12; John 21:25). Furthermore, we have seen that there are passages the exact meaning of which is a matter of ongoing scholarly debate. It is particularly unwise to attempt to "prove" or "disprove" the veracity of Scripture by importing modern, scientific meanings—which are foreign to the text—into the interpretation of Scripture passages. This amounts to a rejection of *sola scriptura*: assumptions outside the Bible are used magisterially to support or reject its content.

A wiser course is to admit that in some cases we do not know the best interpretation of a passage. In other cases, the sense of a passage may be clear, but there is no clear way of *integrating* a claim of Scripture with the claims of

---

[307] *Principles of Biblical Interpretation,* 59.

[308] So Luther distinguishes the inner clarity of faith and the external clarity of Scripture's words. The unbeliever understands the clear assertion of Scripture that God created the heavens and the earth, but rejects it as false because the inner clarity that comes through faith in God is lacking. Pieper quotes Luther as follows: "'If you speak of the inner clearness, no man sees one iota in the Scriptures but he that hath the Spirit of God. All have a darkened heart, so that, even if they know how to speak of, and set forth, all things in the Scripture, yet they cannot feel them or know them; nor do they believe that they are the creatures of God or anything else, according to Psalms 14:1: "The fool hath said in his heart, God is nothing." For the Spirit is required to understand the whole of the Scripture and every part of it. If you speak of the external clearness, nothing whatever is left obscure or ambiguous; but all things that are in the Scriptures are by the Word brought forth into the clearest light and proclaimed to the whole world.'" Pieper, 325. The Luther quotation is from the St. Louis edition, XVIII:1683f. See also Bohlmann, *Principles of Biblical Interpretation,* 59–63.

modern science. In such situations, we must simply do our best to offer an interpretation of the passage or an explanation of the tension between a scriptural claim and the claims of science, acknowledging that such interpretations and explanations are tentative, yet always showing the extent to which they are grounded in the text itself, which is reliable.

In this, Luther's treatment of certain passages can serve as a helpful model of interpretive and intellectual humility paired with a confidence in Christ which sets His Word above human reason. The following extended citation from John Maxfield's book, *Luther's Lectures on Genesis and the Formation of Evangelical Identity*, summarizes this point well:

> In practice, Luther's belief that the Holy Spirit had spoken in the text of scripture as recorded by Moses led him to reject any stepping away from the text as written, even when it involved contradicting the witness of the church fathers or of reason. For example, when Luther rejected patristic allegorical or figurative interpretations regarding the days of creation in Genesis 1, he concluded his argument by stating, 'If we do not comprehend the reason for this, let us remain pupils and leave the magisterium to the Holy Spirit.' [AE 1:5] Likewise on the issue of the cosmology espoused by the opening chapters of Genesis: 'Moses says with clear words that the waters are above and below the firmament. For this reason I take captive here my understanding and agree with the word even if I do not comprehend it.' [AE 1:26]
>
> Luther's adherence to the clear words of Moses in the text of Genesis is reflected also in what appears to be a most banal genealogical table, namely, the genealogy at the end of chapter 10. The professor told his students that this chapter should be esteemed as 'a mirror in which is seen what we human beings are, namely, creatures so deformed by sin that we do not know our own origin—no, not even God himself, our maker—unless the word of God reveals these (as it were) glimmers of divine light to us from afar.' [AE 2:208–209][309]

Indeed, we should not expect a final synthesis of the ultimate and the penultimate. Efforts in that direction tend either to absolutize the relative (giving a preferred scientific theory the status of Scripture) or to relativize the absolute (reducing Scripture to the level of one among many competing "theories"). It is far more honest and faithful to both the goals and purposes of Scripture and science to accept that we must sometimes live with unresolved tensions, knowing that ultimately our confidence and hope lie not in our perfect knowledge but in Christ. Such areas of tension and temporary uncer-

---

[309] *Sixteenth Century Essays & Studies* 80 (Kirksville, Missouri: Truman State University Press, 2008), 34.

tainty are no threat to one who knows "the love of Christ that surpasses all knowledge" and so is "filled with all the fullness of God" (Eph. 3:19).

5. Conclusion

In this chapter, we have attempted to situate the discussion about the proper way to understand the claims of Scripture and science by considering the nature of sound biblical exegesis and its implication for scriptural texts of scientific import. We have emphasized the vital importance of defending the inspiration, infallibility, and inerrancy of Scripture, and we have argued that Scripture is clear in all of its teachings concerning salvation and the Christian life, even if the exact meaning of certain specific texts may be a matter of scholarly dispute. We have discouraged any attempt to use science as a normative standard to either support or correct Scripture. Scripture alone is the ultimate source and norm for all teaching, and the proper role of science, as of reason in general, is to serve as a minister to the faith. It may help us to apply scriptural teaching and, in some cases, it may help us understand what Scripture is saying, but it should never simply be read into the Bible anachronistically. Rather we must follow the often arduous path of humbling ourselves to the original intended meaning of the text. This is where we meet the Christ about whom all the Scriptures testify, and this is where we find our life and salvation.

Chapter V
Practical Applications

1. Introduction

Science provides both opportunities and challenges for thoughtful Christians in a variety of vocations. How should *students* respond to being taught a theory in apparent tension with their faith? How should *teachers* present a controversial scientific idea? How should scientific *investigators* understand their responsibilities? And how should *non-scientific laity* respond to the claims made on behalf of the scientific community by the media and popular books and articles? In this chapter, we will begin to address these questions by discussing how each of these vocational groups might handle some representative (and in some cases, intentionally provocative) examples. In the process, some general principles and rules of thumb will be offered to guide Christian reflection. This chapter does not attempt to speak definitively, but rather encourages an ongoing and constructive discussion in Bible classes and other Christian education venues.[310] It is particularly helpful if the discussion includes both theologically and scientifically trained individuals.[311]

2. Students

A common enough experience for Christian students in high school and college is to be presented with a scientific theory that appears to conflict with their faith. Probably the most common examples derive from evolutionary claims about the origin and diversity of life, for example the assertions that life arose from non-life via undirected natural processes (chemical evolution),

---

[310] Specialized Bible classes on the scientific vocation would be one starting point. See, for example, Robert Weise, *Playing God* (St. Louis: Concordia Publishing House, 2002); Adam Francisco and Jesse Yow, *Off the Edge: Faith, Science, and the Future* (St. Louis: Concordia Publishing House, 2003); and Angus Menuge, *Science and the Savior: The Calling of a Scientist* (St. Louis: Concordia Publishing House, 2004).

[311] It is unfortunate that advanced scientific training has become highly secularized, and Christian science educators and professionals are often not provided classes in the history, philosophy, and theology of science. While some do compensate for this by significant outside reading, the ideal solution is for the church and its universities to provide resources (books, websites, conferences, seminars, etc.) to assist Christian scientists in these areas, allowing them a safe place to think through the intersection of their faith and their scientific work. For this same reason, faith and science classes in Christian high schools and colleges, presentations and discussions at national youth group meetings, district and circuit level pastoral convocations, and conferences for Christian scientific educators and professionals would all be beneficial ways to foster healthy interaction. A book that attempts to model such interaction between scientists, theologians, and historians and philosophers of science is Menuge, *Reading God's World*. One of the most accessible integrations of the history, philosophy, and theology of science is Pearcey and Thaxton's *The Soul of Science*.

and that all of the diversity in the body plans of various creatures derives from descent with modification from a common ancestor via natural selection (so-called macro-evolution). Both in textbooks and in the presentation of many instructors, the impression is given that this is something nature did all by itself, and that, while the student may choose to believe in God, He can have nothing to do with the scientific explanation of the origin and diversity of life.

Unsurprisingly, but unfortunately, many students react to such claims in a number of unhelpful ways that reflect the inadequate solutions to the question of how Christ relates to culture, an issue discussed in chapter 1 of this report. They may come to see science as simply a threat to their faith, as a rival religion or ideology, and thus as something that must be ignored or completely rejected (Christ against Culture). Or they may come to think that the faith must simply be modified so that it is compatible with what any widely accepted scientific theory claims (Christ of Culture). Or it may be thought that the faith must somehow be united with the science (Christ above Culture) or that Christians must improve on the science so that it properly reflects Christian truth (Christ the Transformer of Culture).

However, in one way or another, all of these approaches represent (or risk) a failure of Christian critical engagement. As Gene Edward Veith argues, there are more constructive ways for Christians to respond to problematic ideas, whether from the sciences or from other disciplines.[312] Before responding in any way to a claim made on behalf of science, we should get some critical distance and ask some questions:

(1) To what extent has a purely scientific theory or observation been combined with non-scientific ideologies or philosophical assumptions?

(2) Can we distinguish and disentangle the science from the ideology and the philosophy, and if so, how much of our disagreement is primarily with the latter and not the former?

(3) Even if we still think that the purely scientific claim is overstated and/or false, is there an element of truth in it?

(4) Can we distinguish domains and applications where the claim is useful (and perhaps true) from others where it is more questionable (perhaps because it is untested, or even untestable, in those areas)?

By considering questions like these, a Christian student can achieve a good balance between several vocational objectives. Students are called into the world to serve their neighbor. One reason they should learn about the world's theories is that their neighbor will be exposed to them; such learning is therefore necessary to understanding the neighbor's thinking. We cannot

---

[312] See Veith, "The University of Babylon," chapter 3 in his *Loving God With All Your Mind*.

talk to our neighbor about an issue we do not understand. If she sees evolutionary theory (for example) as a reason to reject God, the gentleness and respect required of Christian witnesses (1 Pet. 3:16) should motivate us to seek to understand the theory that has led to her rejection.

Christian students should also learn about these theories so that, by asking such questions as above, they begin to sift them and to separate out true and false, scientific and ideological, useful and speculative. They are called to be in the world, but not of it, so while learning about the world's ideas and theories, they should also maintain a healthy critical distance from them.

For example, Christian students of science can point out that it is simply not true that any scientific experiment demonstrates abiogenesis (the emergence of life from non-life), and they can note that the strongest evidence for evolutionary theory derives from examples of microevolution (e.g., increased resistance to antibiotics and pesticides). The case for macroevolution, on the other hand, is much more speculative, and not demonstrable by direct observations or experiments. They can also point out that the assumption that nature produces life and its diversity all by itself is fundamentally philosophical, not scientific: it reflects the philosophy of naturalism, according to which nature is an autonomous machine sufficient to account for anything which occurs within itself. Thus anyone who believes that the world was created by God, that God is providentially at work in the world, and that He intervenes in that world through special miracles, must reject this philosophical assumption.

That does not mean Christian students are, or should be, closed to all empirical investigation of the existence and diversity of life. A Christian scientist can develop models of the observable evidence without supposing that those models can settle all the philosophical questions about the ultimate origin and governance of the world. And if some scientists suggest that evidence points to the non-existence of God, there is no reason Christian scientists cannot dispute this, either by critiquing the limitations of that evidence, or by offering other evidence that points in the opposite direction. It is obviously unfair and ideologically biased to claim that scientific evidence can be used to support atheistic conclusions but cannot be used to support theistic ones. Apologetic arguments about science seem unsuited to provide "proof" in some ultimate sense, since science by its nature is a fallible study of a contingent universe. Such arguments are highly valuable, however, in showing that thoughtful Christians can make room for faith in a scientific world.

At the same time, within those domains for which evolutionary theory is useful (and perhaps true), such as understanding micro-evolutionary change in malaria or HIV, Christians intent on a medical career should certainly learn this information, as it may help them in treating patients or in fundamental lab research for more effective drugs and potential cures. Using some aspect of a theory that is helpful is not the same as endorsing all that the theory claims, or all that is claimed for it by proponents of ideologies and philosophies in tension with a Christian worldview. In these ways, a critical sifting of a scientific claim that rejects its non-scientific pretensions to ultimate truth and notes which parts of it are (and are not) supported by evidence, can be combined with a constructive use of the theory whenever it is demonstrably beneficial for the neighbor.

In this way, Christian students of science can balance two important objectives. They can remain faithful, refusing to make a scientific theory into an idol by giving it the ultimate allegiance owed to God alone. They can also develop an appropriate and authentically scientific attitude, one which both properly emphasizes the limits and fallibility of scientific understanding, while at the same time also thoroughly masters current scientific models and the best ways to use them to produce helpful results. There is no reason to choose between being a faithful Christian and developing an exemplary scientific attitude. If young Christians understand this, it will encourage more of them to pursue scientific vocations.

3. Teachers

For this reason, a critical goal for Christian science teachers must be to encourage their Christian students to see that they can pursue scientific careers without compromising their faith. Indeed, the Christian teacher has a responsibility to avoid imparting an anti-scientific perspective to students. Rather, the practical blessings that have accrued to humanity from science and scientists deserve emphasis from Christians because of the centrality of love for the neighbor in Christian theology.

Scientific advances in medicine are an obvious beginning point for the Christian teacher to encourage students toward scientific vocations. Science's steady progress against infectious diseases, infant and maternal mortality, disruption and disease of vital organs, and countless other human scourges and illnesses is so widespread, and its theoretical and technological advances have become so commonplace that we often fail to realize the enormity of their benefits. Moreover, the theological truth that we are saved through faith in Christ alone dare not lead us to disparage the importance of human intellect, research in science and other fields, and the growth of knowledge in general. Central aspects of the scientific method—for example, the importance of privileging evidence over assumptions and the value of critical, careful, objective research and thinking—are vital for every intellectual enterprise.

Rather than discouraging scientific careers and learning, teachers can model integration of faith and learning in their teaching. They can also adopt a pedagogical style that helps students to see how they can learn *about* a scientific claim or theory without either uncritically dismissing or uncritically embracing it. In the process, they will also model good educational practices that allow students to examine all sides of an issue, and avoid indoctrination so that students learn to think for themselves. Precisely because Christians have a place to stand outside of this world, they can be all the more objective in assessing the world's ideas. Standing on Christ and His Word, we do not need to make a scientific theory into a surrogate religion, nor do we have to dismiss it without a due consideration of its benefits for understanding God's world and serving our neighbor.

An exemplary approach here is for science teachers to present controversial ideas by way of *teaching the controversy* itself. That is, in addition to laying out an idea and its implications, students should be encouraged to learn the best arguments that can be given for and against it. This helps students to see that their options are not limited to blank acceptance or rejection of a scientific idea, but it also teaches good critical thinking. Religious and philosophical commitments will always shape our understandings of the world, a fact for which Christian students need not apologize and from which no student or scientist can escape. At the same time, all students, including Christians, will profit by developing the discipline of careful, honest, reasoned inquiry when assessing data and scholarly arguments.

In this way, teachers can assist students in combating erroneous and irrational claims about the authority of scientific ideas that derive from some highly questionable sources, such as the increasing politicization of science and the influence of non-scientific rhetoric in the popular science media. It is sometimes assumed that an idea should be accepted simply because it has been labeled "science"—for example, when we hear sweeping (and often contradictory) assertions that "science shows" what we should (and should not) eat and what is (and is not) good for our health. Science teachers should caution their students to investigate whether there is any supporting data for such claims, how strong it is, and whether there is other research pointing in the same or a different direction. More generally, they should remind their students that scientific claims to have established something with great certainty should, like other human claims, be considered carefully and examined critically.

In presenting a controversial issue—for example, climate change—an exemplary approach is to include the best arguments on all sides of the controversy. Students should be acquainted with the various reports of the United Nations' Intergovernmental Panel on Climate Change (IPCC). They should also be aware of some of criticisms of the claims made by the IPCC and other scientists who accept anthropogenic climate change.[313] It may also be helpful for students to consider the practical implications of the debate,

---

[313] The 2014 report of the IPCC is available at: http://www.ipcc.ch/report/ar5/wg2/. There is also significant literature by scientists who are unconvinced by the claims of the IPCC and others. For example, see Lawrence Solomon's *The Deniers*, rev. ed.(Minneapolis: Richard Vigilante Books, 2010). It is important to note that science, like other academic pursuits, including theology, is often motivated and influenced not only by the pursuit of truth but also by questions of funding, political trends, pressure from peers, and other factors.

such as cost-benefit analyses of both failing to act to abate rising temperatures on one side and aggressive abatement measures on the other.

For example, Bjorn Lomberg, who accepts anthropogenic climate change, argues against diverting vast amounts of money to climate abatement measures, because of a low likelihood of success, negative economic impact, and the danger of chronic underfunding of measures to reduce suffering from malaria, AIDS, and unsafe drinking water that have a solid track record.[314] Such a perspective may help students to consider our global stewardship obligations, rather than focusing on a single "hot topic." This is helpful to Christians because we need to reflect on the overall impact of our actions for the welfare of our neighbors in present and future generations. An ideal situation is one in which students can hear out the best arguments on all sides of the controversy, examine the relevant data, and develop an informed opinion about which claims are best supported by the available evidence.

Certainly, evolutionary theory lends itself to a "teach the controversy" approach that would help students to sift empirical science from ideology and consider the best arguments for and against various evolutionary claims. By focusing on how scientific claims can be confirmed or tested, and showing the relative strengths and weaknesses of various ideas, this approach to science education helps students to see the fallibility and limitations of scientific claims and arguments and has the clear educational objective of promoting critical thinking and objectivity.

For example, students will benefit from supplementing a full and accurate presentation of modern neo-Darwinian evolutionary theory and its supporting evidences with a thoughtful critique by credentialed scientists.[315] It is also very helpful for science educators to consider the insights of leading philosophers of science. Christian science teachers do their students a great service when they point out how different the data can look from the perspective of different fundamental assumptions about how science operates and what it allows. Even if it is not possible to pursue such discussions in class, educators can at least advise students of the existence of dissenting opinions and make them aware of good materials they can consult on their own time.

4. Investigators

Scientists working at universities, government agencies, and private companies should be encouraged toward deep reflection on the vocation of scientist. It is invaluable to spend time considering how great Christian scien-

---

[314] Bjorn Lomberg, *The Skeptical Environmentalist's Guide to Global Warming* (New York: Alfred A. Knopf, 2007).

[315] Again, there is a vast literature, but some excellent recent sources are: Behe, *The Edge of Evolution*; Meyer, *Signature in the Cell* (New York: HarperOne, 2009); and *Darwin's Doubt* (New York: HarperOne, 2013).

tists conceived of their work in previous centuries. Even more vital is the need to recapture the idea that the Bible deeply affirms science as a God-pleasing contribution to our primary vocation of stewardship, and to encourage scientists to delight in their work as they read God's book of nature. As we have seen throughout this report, there are many reasons why thoughtful Christians should want to pursue science as means of glorifying God and serving their neighbor. The eminently practical nature of most scientific work is worth emphasizing. On a daily basis scientists and scientific discoveries help sick people to recover, provide comfort and relief from pain, facilitate healthy and abundant food production, contribute to functional and comfortable living and working spaces, enable speedy and safe transportation, identify criminals (while exonerating others), explore mysteries of space and time—and countless other examples of human betterment. These scientific advances are not simply of technical or theoretical value—they actually serve human beings, people loved and created by God.

In addition to historical reflection on the dignity of the scientific enterprise, scientists will be enriched by deep theological reflection on the nature of the scientific task. How is science affected by the fact that the world is a creation of God? What difference does it make to scientific investigation that scientists themselves are made in the image of God? How does the fall impact the faculties of the scientist? How do we find that middle way, discussed in chapter 2, between excessive modesty and unwarranted pride?

One helpful issue to consider is the way the nature of vocation defines important moral parameters for scientific work. Every vocation exists to serve the neighbor and is bound by God's moral law. In addition, because each vocation has a distinct place within God's economy (it defines a particular contribution to the social and moral order), it has special privileges and special responsibilities. Thus the brain surgeon has the special privilege of doing invasive brain surgery and the special responsibility of doing so in constructive ways. More generally, due to their expertise, scientists are authorized to do things that non-scientists (or scientists with different gifts and training) are not authorized to do; but they also have special responsibilities. Scientists occupy important positions of trust: they are stationed by God to love and serve their neighbor in ways that are beyond the ability of most of us.

As Christian scientists reflect on the moral issues that arise in their work, it is important that they do not ignore the rich resources provided in Scripture and centuries of reflection on Christian ethics. Failure to do so makes it very likely that secular standards of professional ethics will be uncritically embraced as "best practices" within a given area of science. This shortchanges scientists, who are not thereby motivated and encouraged by the understanding that theirs is a high and worthy calling to do good. And there is evidence that a low, pragmatic view of science is bad for the scientific community and those whom it serves. When scientific work is reduced to the quest for maximum funding and fame, it is not surprising that the scientific vocation is corrupted.

For example, in 2012, the *Guardian* newspaper published a series of articles on the way science funding and university policies have conspired to produce an epidemic of scientific fraud, including fabricated data, skewed statistical analysis, and references to non-existent studies and journals:

> A recent paper in the journal *Proceedings of the National Academy of Sciences* shows that since 1973, nearly a thousand biomedical papers have been retracted because someone cheated the system. That's a massive 67% of all biomedical retractions. And the situation is getting worse—last year, *Nature* reported that the rise in retraction rates has overtaken the rise in the number of papers being published.[316]

A major concern is that scientists are a community and each scientist relies on the work of others. Fraudulent research may perpetuate false and dangerous ideas, inhibiting scientific progress and encouraging risky procedures and treatments for human subjects and patients. Here it is important to recover the idea that scientists are called to serve their peers and others by following the highest standards of honesty and integrity in their work.

What is more, secular professional codes of ethics have not always had a high view of the human beings that science affects. This is particularly troubling in the medical sciences and other areas of human experimentation. A Christian understanding of scientific vocation should bring with it a high view of human dignity and value, and should guard against the cynical and unbiblical view that some people are more valuable than others. Human persons are more than biological, psychological, and sociological resources to be valued only for their capacities and contributions to society. Rather, each person is a priceless gift of God.

The general concern is that as human beings are increasingly used as experimental subjects, they may be, consciously or unconsciously, reduced to experimental material. In *The Magician's Nephew*, C. S. Lewis voices this concern through the character of Uncle Andrew, and exposes the corrupt double standard that can allow a scientist to exalt himself into an élite category while reducing other human beings to objects of investigation. In the story, Uncle Andrew tricks two children, Polly and Digory, into wearing magic rings that transport them to a different world, even though he has no idea whether the world will be safe and he is risking the children's lives to satisfy his own curiosity. Uncle Andrew feels justified in this because he thinks scientists have a

---

[316] Pete Etchells and Suzi Gage, "Scientific Fraud is Rife: It's Time to Stand Up for Good Science," *The Guardian*, Friday, November 2, 2012, available at: http://www.theguardian.com/science/blog/2012/nov/02/scientific-fraud-good-science.

superior calling to anyone else's: "Ours ... is a high and lonely destiny."[317] And he has come to see that dumb animals are not as useful as human beings for the experiment he is doing: "I wanted two children. You see I'm in the middle of a great experiment. I've tried it on a guinea-pig and it seemed to work. But then a guinea-pig can't tell you anything. And you can't explain to it how to get back."[318]

Uncle Andrew does not value Polly as a human being made in the image of God but only because her ability to communicate helps his experiment. When Digory rebukes him for sending Polly into a world that he could have investigated for himself, Uncle Andrew's response is revealing:

> "Me? Me?..... A man at my time of life, and in my state of health, to risk the shock and danger of being flung suddenly into a different universe? .... Do you realize what you are saying? Think what Another World means—you might meet any-thing—anything."[319]

Lewis goes on to skewer the double standard that allows Uncle Andrew to defend his own dignity and value while denying it to others. When Uncle Andrew meets a more powerful person, Jadis of Charn (who becomes the White Witch in *The Lion, the Witch and the Wardrobe*), he does not appreciate being reduced to her slave. As philosopher Immanuel Kant would argue, the problem with the idea that a scientist has a special privilege to use others as experimental material is that it cannot be universalized. The scientist would not appreciate being used as material for another scientist's experiment.

Lewis's example is fictional, but there are many painfully real examples of how such thinking has allowed horrific scientific abuses. One need only think of the Nazi eugenic experiments under Adolph Hitler. Science's noble calling was corrupted and men of science rationalized their evil by character-izing it as routine and socially expedient. Such a grim historical episode is not a condemnation of science by any means, but it is a cautionary reminder that every person and every human enterprise is susceptible to the corruption of sin.[320]

Another cautionary example of the danger of science separated from a high regard for human dignity and value is the notorious Tuskegee syphilis study of African-American men in the twentieth century (1932–1972). Patients gave no consent to the experiment, which left them untreated for a deadly

---

[317] C. S. Lewis, *The Magician's Nephew* (New York: Harper Trophy, 1994), 21.

[318] Ibid., 15–16.

[319] Ibid., 25.

[320] Robert Jay Lifton, *The Nazi Doctors: Medical Killing and the Psychology of Genocide* (New York: Basic Books, 1986).

disease, even after penicillin became available and could have provided treatment and cure. [321]

Another example that is more contemporary (and also socially and politically controversial) is embryonic stem cell research. In such research, human embryos—human beings in the earliest stage of human life—are not treated as human beings or afforded the value of human life, but rather as a fitting subject for scientific research and experimentation. While human knowledge might be expanded in the process and some future suffering might be alleviated, such "research" cannot be morally sanctioned.[322]

One lesson that can be learned from these abuses of science is that science is never an excuse to deny the humanity and dignity of another person. The terms "subject" or "patient" must not be allowed to create the illusion that a person made in the image of God is merely a constituent of an experiment that will serve the interests of humanity as a collective or abstract entity. We must resist the temptation to conflate *a person who is sick* (physically or mentally) with *an incidence of a sickness*. Patients notice and appreciate caring doctors who take them seriously as persons—persons who happen to have a health condition—rather than treating them as "statistics" with a pattern of symptoms.

The Christian concept of vocation is again helpful here, as it reminds us that it is not our own interests but the interests of the neighbor that compel us to service in and through our various vocations. In Jesus' parable, the good Samaritan did not view the robbery victim as a crime statistic or offer aid in the hope of advancing his personal projects. Instead, he put the victim's welfare first, and then used the results of the available medical science to serve that person's needs:

> But a Samaritan, as he journeyed, came to where he was, and when he saw him, he had compassion. He went to him and bound up his wounds, pouring on oil and wine. Then he set him on his own animal and brought him to an inn and took care of him. (Luke 10:33-34)

So also the Christian who works in the sciences can see and understand that Christian faith and love motivate a concerted emphasis on using his or her abilities and skill for the well-being of human beings, who are created by God and endowed with dignity from Him. Such a scientist will not give up on the task of research and study, but will carry out his or her daily calling within the moral parameters of biblical theology. So, for example, a Christian medical researcher may indeed carry out stem cell research, but will choose to

---

[321] James Jones, *Bad Blood: The Tuskegee Syphilis Experiment*, New and Expanded ed. (New York: The Free Press, 1993).

[322] Cf. CTCR, *Christian Faith and Human Beginnings: Christian Care and Pre-Implantation Human Life* (2005); available at http://www.lcms.org/Document.fdoc?src=lcm&id=353.

study the possibilities presented by research on umbilical or adult stem cells rather than embryonic stem cells.

As modern life becomes increasingly professionalized, regimented, bureaucratic, and mediated by impersonal technology, it is important to consider whether we are losing contact with the real people that God has called us to serve, and to be intentional about maintaining the genuine love, compassion, and concern for others that Christ embodies and commends. It is not only scientists, but all of us, who suffer alienation from one another through the proliferation of bureaucratic forms, the obsession with statistics, and the distancing of technology. As God became a real man and dwelt among us, speaking words of love and offering both physical and spiritual healing, we must first and foremost minister to real people with our real presence for their real good. We need to ask ourselves, "Am I helping someone today? Or am I only adding data for a report that helps my career or maintains my institution's viability?" If Christ had taken the latter attitude, he might have presented His Father with an impressive study of the state of human sin, but done nothing to heal it. Thanks be to God that Christ so loved us that He came in person, to bear our sins and take the punishment that we deserve, so that we may approach the throne of grace in confidence (Heb. 4:16). This is the pattern, putting the good of other people first, that we must emulate in science and everywhere else.

5. Non-scientists

Science affects everyone in modern societies, not merely because it develops the technologies and treatments we all use, but because it has emerged as a voice of cultural authority relevant to many of our most important decisions. However, this also creates a vulnerability for the non-scientist who is exposed to a cacophony of politically and ideologically charged claims made on behalf of science and, allegedly, with scientific approval or support.

One recommendation for non-scientists is that they learn discernment when they hear reports in the popular science media, especially if they overstate the degree of certainty possible in science, or if they are linked to an ideological agenda. As is true of all human beings, scientists have many non-scientific beliefs and may wish to use the cultural authority of science to support those beliefs. In the process, sober scientific findings are typically conjoined with controversial philosophical assumptions. For example, when the New Atheists declare that supernatural religious belief can be explained away, their background assumption is that religious belief is false. Thus, their speculative naturalistic accounts of religious belief—appealing to a "God spot" in the brain, or a "mind-virus," etc.—seem plausible, despite the lack of supporting data or serious testing.

As one example, consider New Atheist Richard Dawkins's attempt to explain away supernatural religious belief.

Natural selection builds child brains with a tendency to believe whatever their parents and tribal elders tell them. Such trusting obedience is valuable for survival: the analogue of steering by the moon for a moth. But the flip-side of trusting obedience is slavish gullibility. The inevitable by-product is vulnerability to infection by mind viruses... [T]he truster has no way of distinguishing good advice from bad.[323]

Dawkins theorizes that religion can be understood "as a by-product of normal psychological dispositions,"[324] perhaps as "a by-product of the irrationality mechanisms that were originally built into the brain by selection for falling in love."[325] It is a useful form of self-deception because it enables communities to cooperate under some shared goals and guidelines, thus promoting survival.

One major problem for Dawkins's argument is that he attempts to apply a universal rule only selectively. If it is true that our brains are configured by evolution to slavishly trust our elders, and that we have no way of distinguishing good advice from bad, then this would have to include the advice of scientists, especially as they increasingly function as the elders of modern technological societies. In other words, if Dawkins's account of our brains is correct, then we can have no good reason to believe it, since we are in no position to distinguish this truth from error.

A second and purely logical flaw in debunking accounts of religious (or moral) ideas is exposed by C. S. Lewis in his essay "Bulverism." Lewis pointed out that offering an account which might "explain away" why someone has a belief simply bypasses the question of whether the belief is true. That question can only be settled by investigation of the world outside people's minds and brains. Before the skeptic can legitimately claim that religious ideas derive from a tainted source, he must first show that they have no supporting evidence, or provide more compelling evidence against them.

> In other words, you must first show *that* a man is wrong before you start explaining *why* he is wrong. The modern method is to assume without discussion *that* he is wrong and then distract his attention from this (the only real issue) by busily explaining how he became so silly.[326]

After all, no one would take seriously the idea that general relativity is false because modern brain-scanning techniques have shown what is really going on in a physicist's brain when he uses the theory to make predictions

---

[323] Dawkins, *The God Delusion*, 176.

[324] Ibid., 177.

[325] Ibid., 185.

[326] C. S. Lewis, "Bulverism," in *God in the Dock*, 2nd ed., Walter Hooper, ed., (Grand Rapids: Eerdmans, 1970), 273.

or conduct experiments. It is only because Dawkins has made the prior philosophical assumption that supernatural religious claims are false that he spends so little effort looking into the evidence.

The same general moral applies to a variety of other debunking strategies, such as the attempt to explain away religious experiences as a defect in the temporal lobes, the result of a "God gene" or of a misfiring "God-spot" in the brain. All of them assume without argument that no religion is grounded in evidence. Yet the central Christian claims are about Christ's saving work in *history*, and therefore can be investigated using secular, empirical methods. In their book, *The Spiritual Brain*, neuroscientist Mario Beauregard and science journalist Denyse O'Leary provide a wonderful antidote to many of the overblown claims of secularists in the popular science media, and expose many of the recurring, unexamined philosophical assumptions that drive agenda-driven claims about what science shows.[327]

More generally, a good strategy when engaging any material using science to advocate for non-Christian conclusions is to consult the best evaluation of that work (for example, in book reviews, articles, or on blogs) from a qualified Christian thinker. Invariably what emerges is that when scientists seek to use science to discredit Christianity or theism in general, it is their non-scientific philosophical assumptions, and not the scientific data, that play the decisive role.

As one more example of this, consider a recent work by the atheist cosmologist, Lawrence Krauss, *A Universe From Nothing*.[328] Krauss's goal is to use modern cosmology to show that God is not necessary to explain the origin of the universe. In the course of the book, Krauss offers three scientific definitions of "nothing," and argues that each of them allow the universe to arise from nothing, without God. Thus in chapter 9, "nothing" means empty space, which Krauss tells us, can expand and produce matter and radiation. In chapter 10, Krauss goes further, and defines "nothing" as the *absence of space*, in which "quantum gravity... might create an inflating universe directly from nothing."[329] And finally, in chapter 11, "nothing" is defined as the absence of the laws of physics, which laws might somehow arise at random from a multiverse.[330]

The problem with Krauss's approach is that in every case, he has altered the standard definition of "nothing." Logicians understand "nothing" as a universal negation: to say "Nothing is there" is equivalent to saying, "Given all of the things that exist, none of them is there." By that understanding,

---

[327] See Mario Beauregard and Denyse O'Leary, *The Spiritual Brain: A Neuroscientist's Case for the Existence of the Soul* (New York: HarperCollins, 2007).

[328] See fn 32, p. 17 above.

[329] Krauss, *A Universe From Nothing*, 169.

[330] Ibid., 176.

empty space is not nothing, since nothing cannot expand. Likewise quantum gravity and, if it exists, the multiverse, are not nothing. Nothing has no potential to do anything. Thus a bad essay can be improved, but a non-existent essay cannot. Only what exists has the potential to produce any further result.

The real issue here is not scientific at all. It is a matter of metaphysics. An atheist thinks that the universe (or a multiverse) simply exists as a brute fact, whereas a theist thinks that the existence of the universe requires some explanation, and argues that this is provided by a supernatural, necessary being. Krauss ignores this reality because he dismisses all "philosophical and theological musings,"[331] and believes that science is the only source of knowledge. But the result is that Krauss is simply unaware of his own philosophical assumptions (such as scientism and naturalism). He is therefore unable to see that the origin of the universe is a profoundly philosophical question that cannot be adequately addressed without metaphysics.

C. S. Lewis frequently admonished Christians to read old books,[332] not because the old books are always right, and newer books are always wrong, but because the older books contain a valuable counter-perspective, preserving insights that our own age ignores. Contemporary debates about the role of science in public life and what this implies is often poorly informed by a sound historical perspective on the development of science and the interaction of science with theology and philosophy. Thus, when Krauss asserts that, unlike modern science, "theology has made no contribution to knowledge,"[333] a well-informed Christian may respond that one cannot pit science against theology, because, in point of historical fact, modern science was in large measure an outgrowth of theology.

Assumptions made by all scientists today—including atheist and other non-Christian scientists—reflect a view of reality that derives from theological sources. Scientists are able to search for universal laws of nature because they presuppose that nature is a coherent, law-governed system—an assumption grounded in the theological idea that the world is the product of a single, rational Creator. Scientists make observations and conduct experiments to find out what is going on in natural world (rather than deducing its behavior from a preconceived philosophy) because they assume that world is contingent—an idea grounded in the theological idea that the world is the creation of a free being who might have created differently. Scientists are confident that they can discover the truth because there is objective truth in the world to discover and their own minds are reliably attuned to that truth. These, too, are assumptions ultimately grounded in the theological idea that the divine logos is reflected both in nature and in the minds of those made in God's image.

---

[331] Ibid., 143.

[332] Lewis, "On the Reading of Old Books," in *God in the Dock*.

[333] Krauss, *A Universe From Nothing*, 144.

More generally, non-scientists will benefit greatly from reading widely in the history, theology, and philosophy of science. This will quickly reveal the fact that science is not done in a vacuum, but is always influenced by a complex variety of non-scientific beliefs. By becoming aware of these beliefs, one can more effectively disentangle the science proper from other ideas that may motivate science and may be used to evaluate its findings. When it is confidently claimed that pursuing science requires abandoning many Christian ideas as outmoded, superstitious relics of our pre-scientific past, Christians can simply point out the great contributions of historical and contemporary scientists who not only accepted Christian doctrine, but who found it to be a source of encouragement and support.[334] Indeed, the history of science is filled with stories of men and women who viewed faith in God as a motivation and source of strength for their calling. Countless members of the scientific community today share such convictions (they are hardly outdated!) and, God willing, their numbers will increase.

6. Conclusion

While much more could be said, it is hoped that the examples and discussion in this chapter will help to motivate further reading, classes and discussion that will benefit Christian students, teachers, researchers and non-scientific laity. If we reflect on the interdependence of our different vocations, and apply that insight specifically to science, it may generate more Bible studies, seminars, convocations and conferences that bring these groups of people together with our clergy and other professional church workers to discuss the most constructive Christian responses to science, its findings, and the claims made on its behalf.

In the process, we can encourage more Christians to pursue careers and vocations in science, confident of their calling and with a high moral motivation. We can also aid students and teachers, seeking the best strategies for handling controversy, especially as it impacts on the Christian faith. And we can see scientists themselves as a great resource in the body of Christ, those best qualified to help us understand what science is really saying and best equipped to inspire young people to follow them into scientific vocations. Together with the other resources in this report, it is hoped this final chapter will promote more constructive dialogue about the intersection of science and Christian theology.

---

[334] An excellent place to begin is Stanley Jaki's accessible yet learned work, *The Savior of Science*. There is also a recent assessment of Jaki's enormous contribution to understanding the interplay of science and the Christian faith by Stacy Trasancos, *Science was Born of Christianity: The Teaching of Fr. Stanley L. Jaki* (Titusville, FL: The Habitation of Chimham Publishing, 2014).